INTERNATIONAL SERIES OF MONOGRAPHS ON
ORGANIC CHEMISTRY
GENERAL EDITORS: D. H. R. BARTON and W. DOERING

VOLUME 5

APPLICATIONS OF NUCLEAR MAGNETIC RESONANCE SPECTROSCOPY IN ORGANIC CHEMISTRY

OTHER TITLES IN THE SERIES ON ORGANIC CHEMISTRY

Vol. 1. WATERS—*Vistas in Free Radical Chemistry*

Vol. 2. TOPCHIEV ET AL.—*Boron Fluoride and its Compounds as Catalysts in Organic Chemistry*

Vol. 3. JANSSEN—*Synthetic Analgesics–Part I: Diphenylpropylamines*

Vol. 4. WILLIAMS—*Homolytic Aromatic Substitution*

Applications of
Nuclear Magnetic Resonance
Spectroscopy
in Organic Chemistry

by

L. M. JACKMAN

Lecturer in Organic Chemistry,
Imperial College of Science and Technology,
London

PERGAMON PRESS
NEW YORK · OXFORD · LONDON · PARIS

0151
PERGAMON PRESS INC.,
122 East 55th Street, New York 22, N.Y.

PERGAMON PRESS LTD.,
Headington Hill Hall, Oxford.
4 and 5 Fitzroy Square, London, W.1.

PERGAMON PRESS S.A.R.L.
24 Rue des Écoles, Paris V^e.

PERGAMON PRESS G.m.b.H.
Kaiserstrasse 75, Frankfurt-am-Main.

Copyright

©

1959

Pergamon Press Ltd.

First published 1959
2nd impression 1962

Reproduced by photo-lithography and made at the Pitman Press, Bath

CONTENTS

                                          PAGE

FOREWORD   vii

EDITORIAL PREFACE   viii

AUTHOR'S PREFACE   ix

1. INTRODUCTION AND HISTORICAL REVIEW

1.1 Dynamic and magnetic properties of atomic nuclei   1
1.2 The historical background to nuclear magnetic resonance spectroscopy   2
1.3 Nuclear magnetic resonance spectroscopy—past, present and future   4

2. THE THEORY OF NUCLEAR MAGNETIC RESONANCE SPECTROSCOPY

2.1 Nuclear resonance   6
2.2 Relaxation processes   8
2.3 Saturation   13
2.4 Magnetic shielding of atomic nuclei   14
2.5 Electron coupled spin–spin interactions   20
2.6 Chemical exchange and hindered rotation   26

3. THE EXPERIMENTAL METHOD

3.1 The nuclear magnetic resonance spectrometer—A brief description   30
3.2 The magnet   30
3.3 The radiofrequency oscillator   31
3.4 The magnetic field sweep   32
3.5 The detector   33
3.6 Experimental factors which influence nuclear magnetic resonance spectra   35
3.7 Calibration of spectra and the determination of shielding values   41
3.8 Solvents   48
3.9 Measurement of intensities   48

4. THE CORRELATION OF THE CHEMICAL SHIFT WITH MOLECULAR STRUCTURE: HYDROGEN BOUND TO CARBON

4.1 Introduction   50
4.2 Aliphatic protons   51
4.3 Additivity of substituent effects—Shoolery's rules   59
4.4 Olefinic, allenic and acetylenic protons   60
4.5 Aldehydic protons   62
4.6 Aromatic protons in hydrocarbons and heterocycles   62

PAGE

5. THE CORRELATION OF THE CHEMICAL SHIFT WITH MOLECULAR STRUCTURE *(cont.)*

A. *Protons attached to elements other than carbon*
    5.1 Hydrogen attached to oxygen   66
    5.2 Hydrogen attached to nitrogen   72
    5.3 Protons in thiols and metal hydrides   74

B. *Nuclear magnetic resonance of isotopes other than ^1H*   74
    5.4 Fluorine (^{19}F)   75
    5.5 Phosphorus (^{31}P)   77
    5.6 Carbon (^{13}C)   78
    5.7 Nitrogen (^{14}N), Oxygen (^{17}O) and Deuterium (^{2}H)   79

6. THE INTERPRETATION OF THE SPECTRA OF COMPLEX ORGANIC MOLECULES
    6.1 Introduction   82
    6.2 Electron coupled spin–spin interactions   83
    6.3 Internal rotation and the equivalence of nuclei   99
    6.4 Line positions   103
    6.5 Intensities   105
    6.6 Examples   105

7. DIAMAGNETIC ANISOTROPY AND STEREOCHEMISTRY
    7.1 Long-range shielding   112
    7.2 The stereochemistry of cyclohexane and related ring systems   115
    7.3 Geometrical isomerism about carbon–carbon double bonds   119
    7.4 Examples of long-range shielding by the benzene ring   125
    7.5 The diamagnetic anisotropy of the carbon–carbon double bond   129
    7.6 A reconsideration of Shoolery's rules   130

INDEX   131

FOREWORD

NUCLEAR magnetic resonance was first observed in bulk matter in 1945 by Purcell, Torrey and Pound at Harvard University, and Bloch, Hansen and Packard at Stanford University. The spectra were used to study nuclear properties, and the ways in which the nuclei would exchange energy with themselves and with their surroundings. Many fascinating experiments gave new insight into a variety of problems in physics including thermodynamics and subtle details about the properties of solids and liquids.

In 1948, nuclear resonance spectra were applied to the determination of distances between hydrogen atoms in some crystals and to the study of hindered molecular motion in solids. A number of chemical problems of this kind were then solved. In 1949 Knight described the so-called "chemical shifts" in metals, and in 1950 similar effects in chemical substances were described by Proctor and Yu, by Dickinson, by Lindström and by Thomas. Only one year later Arnold, Dharmatti and Packard showed that the hydrogen resonance of alcohol contained three lines, assignable to the CH_3, CH_2 and OH hydrogens. From this time it was clear that nuclear magnetic resonance, discovered only five years earlier, would be of considerable importance to organic chemists.

The methods of observing these high resolution nuclear magnetic resonance spectra have been developed with great rapidity and will, no doubt, receive considerable further refinement to improve the quality and reproducibility of the spectra. The method is already used extensively by chemists for structural determination, for studies of isomerism, reaction rates, molecular interaction and chemical equilibria.

The principles of the method and the interpretation of the results are usually rather simple, but the method can be used efficiently only with the aid of the many results and correlations already described in the literature.

This book is therefore very welcome and describes in a simple way how any organic chemist may understand some of the uses of this technique and interpret the spectra of his compounds.

Lincoln College,
Oxford.

Dr. R. E. RICHARDS, F.R.S.

EDITORIAL PREFACE

PRIOR to 1958, examples of the successful application of nuclear magnetic resonance (n.m.r.) to problems in structural organic chemistry were so few in number that organic chemistry departments could scarcely justify the purchase of expensive high resolution equipment. Now, less than two years later, departments which do not possess an n.m.r. spectrometer are at a considerable disadvantage relative to those where such facilities are available.

This new technique has many obvious, although not always unique, applications to the identification of functional groups. For example, the n.m.r. method can be used to demonstrate the presence or absence of a methyl ketone, a problem which can also be resolved by chemical methods, though with more effort and with the consumption of the compound under investigation. However, the real power of n.m.r. derives from its more subtle features. Thus chemical shift and spin-spin coupling data, when interwoven with the results of chemical experiments, may lead to a simplified solution of even complex structural problems. Indeed the method offers a new fascinating approach to work of this kind.

There are several problems which face the organic chemist who wishes to employ n.m.r. spectroscopy. Firstly he must acquire a working knowledge of the subject. In this respect his theoretical requirements will be of minor importance, but he will need to become familiar with the regions of absorption of protons in the more common organic chemical environments, and with the simpler concepts of spin-spin coupling. This book will satisfy these needs in an exemplary manner. Secondly, he will need to be aware of potential applications of the methods which lie outside his general experience. When such situations arise he will then be able to consult colleagues who are competent to tackle such tasks, for it would be quite unrealistic to expect the practising organic chemist to undertake the mathematical computations required for the analysis of certain complex spectra. The author of this book has carefully drawn attention to this situation and has wisely refrained from interspersing the text with mathematical equations which would render it incomprehensible to most of the intended readers.

It is indeed fortunate that Dr. L. M. Jackman, who has become an expert in n.m.r. spectroscopy, could be persuaded to write a clear and authoritative text suitable for organic chemists. The subject will obviously develop further in the next few years and the present volume is not the final word on progress in this field. Nevertheless, the applications of n.m.r. spectroscopy to organic chemistry are already so numerous and so important that an account of the subject at the present time is certainly justified. Dr. Jackman's book is warmly recommended to all organic chemists and to workers in other disciplines who are interested in any way in organic molecules.

Professor D. H. R. BARTON, F.R.S.

Imperial College of Science and Technology,
London.

TO MARIE

PREFACE

NOWADAYS, the practice of pure organic chemistry requires the use of a number of physical methods, the fundamentals of which belong to the realms of chemical physics. Consequently, organic chemists have come to rely on standard treatises which provide simplified introductions to the theory of such methods, together with compilations of relevant data which can be used for the characterization of organic compounds and for the elucidation of molecular structure and stereo-chemistry. The most recent method to be adopted by the organic chemist is nuclear magnetic resonance spectroscopy and although the widespread use of this technique has only just commenced many workers are already alive to its considerable potential. For this reason there is a need for a text which provides a non-mathematical introduction to the theory and practice of n.m.r. and which provides such classified data as is at present available. In this book I have attempted to satisfy these needs. I have tried to keep the physical background to a minimum since physical concepts often constitute a "potential barrier" to the organic chemist. At the same time I consider that an understanding of the pertinent physical principles is vital if this powerful technique is to be used with maximum effect. Thus, I have tried to present these principles descriptively at the same time providing references for those readers who may wish to pursue the rigorously mathematical approach.

An unfortunate consequence of writing about n.m.r. at such an early stage in its development is that I have had to commit myself and my readers to one specific method of expressing the chemical shift of hydrogen, whereas in fact a number of systems are in current use and several committees are at present deliberating on such matters. The system I have used is that of τ-values introduced by G. V. D. Tiers. I have chosen the method of Tiers because I believe that its simplicity will appeal to organic chemists and because the values for a vast majority of protons in organic molecules lie between zero and ten and are thus readily committed to memory. If an alternative system is adopted by international agreement it must certainly be based on an internal reference so that the data in this book will be readily convertible to the new units.

I have drawn on the chemical literature up till May 1959 but as it appeared desirable to limit this book to its present length I have been able to quote only a few of the many examples of the application of n.m.r. in structural studies.

I consider that one of the principle features of this book is the summarized experimental data which it contains and I am therefore most happy to acknowledge my gratitude to Dr. G. V. D. Tiers of the Minnesota Mining and Manufacturing Co., and Dr. N. F. Chamberlain of the Humble Oil and Refining Company who provided me with their extensive compilations of unpublished data.

Although this book is comparatively short, the list of colleagues to whom I am indebted is long and I am glad of this opportunity to acknowledge their help.

I am particularly grateful to Professor D. H. R. Barton, F.R.S., for granting me the opportunity to work in the field of n.m.r., and indeed it was at his suggestion that I undertook to write this book. He has followed its course with interest and has read the entire manuscript. I owe much to Dr. L. H. Pratt and Dr. D. F. Evans who provided my early education in the subject and who also read part of the manuscript. Dr. R. E. Richards, F.R.S., carefully read the manuscript from the point of view of an n.m.r. spectroscopist and kindly suggested several alterations which I feel have greatly improved the text, while Dr. E. S. Waight and Dr. B. C. L. Weedon read the book as organic chemists and were likewise able to draw my attention to many obscurities. I also received some much appreciated encouragement from Professor W. von E. Doering who read several of the early chapters. Dr. D. W. Turner made helpful criticisms of Chapter 3. I am most grateful to Miss B. A. Harsant for typing the manuscript.

Finally, I am grateful to many authors, to the editors and publishers of the *Journal of the American Chemical Society*, *Helvetica Physica Acta*, the *Annals of the New York Academy of Science*, *Journal of Chemical Physics*, *Molecular Physics*, *Transactions of the Faraday Society*, and to Varian Associates for permission to reproduce diagrams.

July 1959   L. M. JACKMAN

Note added in proof. It is now conventional to present spectra with the field increasing from left to right. With the exception of Figs. 2·15, 5·4, 6·1, 6·2 and 6·16, spectra reproduced herein accord with this convention.

CHAPTER 1

INTRODUCTION AND HISTORICAL REVIEW

1.1 DYNAMIC AND MAGNETIC PROPERTIES OF ATOMIC NUCLEI

APART from the use of atomic numbers and isotopic weights, the organic chemist has largely developed his subject without any special knowledge of the properties of atomic nuclei. The recent advent of nuclear magnetic resonance spectroscopy and, to a much lesser extent, microwave and pure quadrupole spectroscopy, has altered this state of affairs and organic chemists of the present generation have now to become acquainted with certain subjects hitherto the domain of the nuclear physicist and spectroscopist. Thus today a table of atomic weights of those elements commonly encountered by the organic chemist might usefully include other nuclear properties such as spin numbers, nuclear magnetic moments, and nuclear electric quadrupole moments. Of these additional nuclear properties the spin number, I, and the nuclear magnetic moment, μ, are of particular interest; the nuclear electric quadrupole moment, Q, will enter only occasionally into our discussions.

The nuclei of certain isotopes possess an intrinsic mechanical spin; that is they are associated with an angular momentum. The total angular momentum of a nucleus is given by $(h/2\pi).[I(I+1)]$ in which h is Plank's constant and I is the *nuclear spin* or *spin number* which may have the values 0, $\frac{1}{2}$, 1, $\frac{3}{2}$, . . . depending on the particular isotopic nucleus ($I = 0$ corresponds to a nucleus which does not possess a mechanical spin). Since atomic nuclei are also associated with an electric charge, mechanical spin gives rise to a magnetic field such that we may consider a spinning nucleus as a minute bar magnet the axis of which is coincident with the axis of spin.* The magnitude of this magnetic dipole is expressed as the nuclear magnetic moment, μ, which has a characteristic value for all isotopes for which I is greater than zero.

In a uniform magnetic field the angular momentum of a nucleus ($I > 0$) is quantized, the nucleus taking up one of $(2I+1)$ orientations with respect to the direction of the applied field. Each orientation corresponds to a characteristic potential energy of the nucleus equal to $\mu . H_0 . \cos \theta$ where H_0 is the strength of the applied field and the angle θ is the angle which the spin axis of the nucleus makes with the direction of the applied field. The importance of I and μ in our discussion is that they define the number and energies of the possible spin states which the nuclei of a given isotope can take up in a magnetic field of known strength. A transition of a nucleus from one spin state to an adjacent state may occur by the absorption or emission of an appropriate quantum of energy.

---

*The neutron has $I = \frac{1}{2}$ and possesses a magnetic moment even though it has no net charge. This apparent paradox is resolved in terms of Yukawa's dissociation theory in which it is assumed that the neutron, for a fraction of its life-time, is partially dissociated to a proton and negative meson, the magnetic moment of the latter being larger than, and of opposite sign to, that of the former.

Nuclei of isotopes for which $I > \frac{1}{2}$ are usually associated with an asymmetric charge distribution which constitutes an electric quadrupole. The magnitude of this quadrupole is expressed as the nuclear quadrupole moment Q.

Finally in this brief introduction to the properties of spinning nuclei we must consider the behaviour of a nucleus when subjected to a torque which tends to alter the spatial orientation of its axis of rotation. The general behaviour of a rotating body under the influence of a torque acting about an axis perpendicular to the axis of rotation is shown in Fig. 1.1. A torque of this nature does not affect

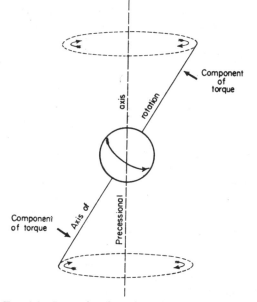

FIG. 1.1   Precessional motion of a rotating body.

the magnitude of the angular velocity of the body but causes the axis of rotation to alter continuously so that each pole of the axis sweeps out a circular path. The imposed motion is called precession* and familiar examples include the behaviour of toy gyroscopes and the precession of the equinoxes. A spinning nucleus will execute precessional motion under the influence of the torque imposed by a uniform magnetic field.

The properties discussed above are the basis of our subject. Now that we have defined them we can describe the sequence of events which has led to the discovery of one of the most powerful aids to organic chemistry and so acknowledge our debt to the physicist.

1.2   THE HISTORICAL BACKGROUND TO NUCLEAR MAGNETIC RESONANCE SPECTROSCOPY

The concepts of nuclear spin and magnetic moment were developed at about the same time as the analogous properties of the electron. Uhlenbeck and Goudsmit[1]

*In accordance with common usage in the literature of nuclear magnetic resonance phenomena we shall employ the verb to *precess* although it does not appear in the O.E.D.

(1925), and Bechowsky and Urey[2] (1926), independently postulated the properties of angular momentum and magnetic moment of the electron in order to account for certain aspects of the fine structure of the atomic hydrogen spectrum. There had been prior suggestions that the electron possessed spin properties, and Pauli[3] in 1924 had even suggested that the hyperfine structure observed in atomic spectra could be explained if it were assumed that the *nuclei* of certain isotopes were associated with a magnetic moment. The idea of electron spin was rapidly accepted and it was not long before convincing experimental confirmation of nuclear spin and magnetic moment was forthcoming. Dennison[4] (1927) showed by heat capacity studies that hydrogen gas was composed of two molecular species (ortho- and para-hydrogen) which differed in the symmetry of their nuclear spin wave functions. Further evidence was obtained by Hund[5] from the rotational structure in the band spectra of homonuclear diatomic gases, and Pauli's original suggestion that nuclear magnetic moments were responsible for the hyperfine structure in the atomic spectra of pure isotopes also received experimental verification.[6]

Thus by the early 1930s the spins and magnetic moments of a number of isotopes had been determined and the following years saw further intensive research in this direction. This period also saw the development of two experimental techniques which ultimately pointed the way to nuclear magnetic resonance spectroscopy. The first of these was the extension by Estermann and Stern[7] of the original Stern–Gerlach experiment to a study of the magnetic deflection of atomic and molecular beams. The magnetic moment of the proton was first determined in this way. The second technique was introduced by Rabi and his co-workers[8] in 1939 and is called the molecular beam resonance technique. In the Estermann–Gerlach experiment a collimated beam of nuclei is split by an inhomogeneous magnetic field into components corresponding to the different spin states of the nuclei, i.e. to different values of I. Rabi's method involves a refocusing technique in which the deflected beam is subjected to a second inhomogeneous field which causes the nuclei to retrace the deflection caused by the first field. If during its passage through the two fields a nucleus changes its spatial orientation (i.e. if it undergoes a transition to another spin state) it will not be refocused, and the essential feature of the molecular beam resonance method is that it permits the detection of nuclear spin transitions. Normally, the number of nuclei which undergo transitions during the passage through the two fields is negligible. However, if prior to refocusing, the deflected beam is passed through a homogeneous magnetic field and simultaneously irradiated with electromagnetic radiation transitions between spin states will occur provided the frequency of the radiation corresponds to the energy difference between the spin states (p. 7). It transpires that for the strengths of the homogeneous field employed in these experiments the correct frequency lies in the radiofrequency region. The exact radiofrequency which will cause the efficiency of refocusing to fall to a minimum is a function of I, μ, and the strength of the homogeneous field, so that if I is known the value of μ can be determined.

We shall see in the next chapter that nuclear magnetic resonance spectroscopy involves the principles embodied in Rabi's method, the difference between the two techniques being of an experimental nature. In the latter method the absorption and emission of radiant energy is observed by virtue of its effect on the nuclei whereas the former technique turns out to be a genuine spectroscopic method in as much as the absorption of electromagnetic energy is detected directly.

1.3 NUCLEAR MAGNETIC RESONANCE SPECTROSCOPY— PAST, PRESENT, AND FUTURE

Molecular beam resonance techniques were used in 1937 to determine the magnetic moment of the neutron[9] and were extended in 1938–1939 to atomic nuclei. The stage was thus set for the entry of nuclear magnetic resonance spectroscopy which was to be a simpler method applicable to all phases of matter. The first attempts directly to observe the absorption of electromagnetic radiation by matter were made by Gorter and Broer[10] in 1942. The substances examined were lithium chloride and potassium fluoride at low temperatures. These experiments were unsuccessful and although the correct reasons for their failure were advanced it was not until four years later that successful experiments were reported by two independent groups, namely Purcell, Torrey and Pound[11] at Harvard, and Bloch, Hansen, and Packard[12] at Stanford University. The impact of these experiments was immediate. For the first few years the method continued to be the province of the physicist and physical chemist and, although in this book we must perforce ignore much of this work, the discoveries and advances during this period make dramatic and exciting reading.[13]

Four or five years after the first successful nuclear magnetic resonance experiments there appeared several reports of a phenomenon which has since proved to be general and of the utmost significance to the organic chemist. It was found[14] that the characteristic absorption frequency of a nucleus in a magnetic field is dependent to a small but measurable extent on the molecular environment of the nucleus. In other words it was now apparent that nuclear magnetic resonance spectroscopy was not only a method for investigating nuclear parameters and certain physico-chemical problems but that it might possibly be useful in studies of molecular structure. The rapidity with which this possibility has become a reality can be gauged by the fact that this and other books dealing with the relation of nuclear magnetic resonance spectroscopy to molecular structure have been written within ten years of the original observations referred to above.

At the present time, nuclear magnetic resonance spectroscopy is finding wide application in organic chemistry although it would be incorrect to say that it is used as frequently as some other spectroscopic methods, for as yet many laboratories are without the necessary equipment. However, those workers who have both access to the method and the experience in interpreting the results cannot fail to agree that nuclear magnetic resonance spectroscopy is an extremely powerful technique.

What then does the future of the method hold for the organic chemist? At present the possibilities seem unlimited. Even if there were no further developments in experimental technique the utility of the method could not fail to increase as our experience extends over greater and greater numbers of organic compounds. Published data refer to less than two thousand compounds, a trifling number when we think of the vast number of spectra on which infrared correlation rules are based. However, on the experimental side great developments are conceivable. Improvements in magnet materials and in spin-decoupling methods (see next chapter) could change the usefulness of the technique by an order of magnitude and thereby reduce the determination of the structures of many compounds to a very simple procedure.

REFERENCES

1. G. E. ULENBECK and S. GOUDSMIT, *Naturwiss.* **13**, 953 (1925).
2. R. BICHOWSKY and H. C. UREY, *Proc. Natl. Acad. Sci.* **12**, 80 (1926).
3. W. PAULI, *Naturwiss.* **12**, 741 (1924).
4. D. M. DENNISON, *Proc. Roy. Soc.* A **115**, 483 (1927).
5. F. HUND, *Z. Physik.* **42**, 93 (1927).
6. S. TOLANSKY, *Hyperfine Structure in Line Spectra and Nuclear Spin*, 2nd ed., Methuen, London, 1948.
7. I. ESTERMANN and O. STERN, *Z. Physik.* **85**, 170 (1933).
8. I. RABI, S. MILLMAN, P. KUSCH and J. R. ZACHARIAS, *Phys. Rev.* **55**, 526 (1939); J. B. M. KELLOGG, I. RABI, N. F. RAMSEY and J. R. ZACHARIAS, *ibid.* **56**, 728.
9. L. W. ALVAREZ and F. BLOCH, *ibid.* **57**, 111 (1940).
10. C. J. GORTER and L. J. F. BROER, *Physica* **9**, 591 (1942).
11. E. M. PURCELL, H. C. TORREY and R. V. POUND, *Phys. Rev.* **69**, 37 (1946).
12. F. BLOCH, W. W. HANSEN and M. PACKARD, *ibid*, **127**.
13. E. R. ANDREW, *Nuclear Magnetic Resonance*, Cambridge University Press, 1955.
14. H. S. GUTOWSKY and C. J. HOFFMAN, *J. Chem. Phys.* **19**, 1259 (1951), and references given therein.

CHAPTER 2

THE THEORY OF NUCLEAR MAGNETIC RESONANCE SPECTROSCOPY

ALTHOUGH the literature contains several detailed mathematical treatments of the theory of nuclear magnetic resonance which are based on microphysical[1,2] or macrophysical[2,3,4] concepts we will be content to develop the theory, as far as possible, in a purely descriptive manner by stating in words the results of the physicists' equations. In doing so we will no doubt lose the elements of exactness but as organic chemists we will gain tangible concepts of considerable utility, which would otherwise be lost to all but those possessing an adequate mathematical background.

2.1 NUCLEAR RESONANCE

The starting point of our discussion is a consideration of a bare nucleus, such as a proton, in a magnetic field of strength H_0. Later we will consider collections of nuclei. We will also add the extranuclear electrons and ultimately we will build the atoms into molecules but we must first consider the simple nucleus. We have already seen that certain nuclei possess two very important properties associated with spin angular momentum. These properties are the spin number I and the magnetic moment μ. We are only concerned with the nuclei of those elements for which these two quantities are not equal to zero. When such a nucleus is placed in a static uniform magnetic field H_0 it may take up one of $(2I+1)$ orientations which are characterized by energies dependent on the magnitudes of μ and H_0. If our bare nucleus is a proton, which has a spin number I equal to one half, we can liken it to a very tiny bar magnet. A large bar magnet is free to take up any possible orientation in the static field so that there are an infinite number of permissible energy states. Quantum mechanics tells us that the tiny proton magnet is restricted to just two possible orientations $[(2I+1)=2]$, in the applied field and these can be considered to be a low energy or parallel orientation in which the magnet is aligned with the field and a high energy or anti-parallel orientation in which it is aligned against the field (i.e. with its N. pole nearest the N. pole of the static field). Since these two orientations correspond to two energy states it should be possible to induce transitions between them and the frequency, ν, of the electromagnetic radiation which will effect such transitions is given by the equation

$$h\nu = \frac{\mu\beta_N \cdot H_0}{I} \tag{1}$$

where β_N is a constant called the nuclear magneton. Equation (1) may be rewritten as (2)

$$\nu = \gamma \cdot H_0/2\pi \tag{2}$$

where γ is known as the gyromagnetic ratio. The absorption or emission of the quantum of energy $h\nu$ causes the nuclear magnet to turn over or "flip" from one orientation to the other. For nuclei with spin numbers greater than $\frac{1}{2}$ there will be more than two possible orientations (3 for $I = 1$, 4 for $I = \frac{3}{2}$, etc.) and in each case a set of equally spaced energy levels results. Again electromagnetic radiation of appropriate frequency can cause transitions between the various levels with the proviso (i.e. selection rule) that only transitions between adjacent levels are allowed. Since the energy levels are equally spaced this selection rule requires that there is only one characteristic transition frequency for a given value of H_0. If we insert numerical values into our equation for ν we find that, for magnetic fields of the order of 10,000 gauss,* the characteristic frequencies lie in the radiofrequency region (ca. 10^7–10^8 c/s). Thus our first primitive picture of nuclear magnetic resonance spectroscopy may be summed up by stating that atomic nuclei of certain elements ($I > 0$) when placed in a strong magnetic field may absorb radiofrequency radiation.

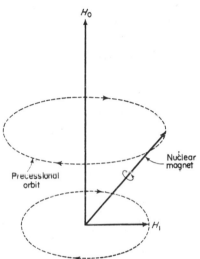

Fig. 2.1   The behaviour of a nuclear magnet in a magnetic field (in this figure the applied field, H_0, the rotating field, H_1, and the nuclear magnetic dipole are represented as vectors).

We shall now develop a classical picture of the absorption process which takes us a little further in our understanding of nuclear magnetic resonance and which provides a useful model for discussing the experimental procedure.   Let us consider our spinning nucleus to be orientated at an angle θ to the direction of the applied field H_0 (Fig. 2.1). The main field acts on the nuclear magnet so as to decrease the angle θ. However, because the nucleus is spinning the net result is that the nuclear magnet is caused to precess about the main field axis. The angular velocity ω_0 of this precessional motion is given by equation (3).

$$\omega_0 = \gamma H_0 = 2\pi\nu \qquad (3)$$

The precessional frequency ω_0 is directly proportional to H_0 and to the gyromagnetic

*The gauss is strictly speaking the unit of magnetic induction and the field strength should be measured in oersteds. In air the two units are almost equivalent and the former is commonly used.

ratio* and is exactly equal to the frequency of electromagnetic radiation which, on quantum mechanical grounds, we decided was necessary to induce a transition from one nuclear spin state to an adjacent level. We are now in the position to establish the exact character of the radiofrequency radiation necessary to do this. The act of turning over the nucleus from one orientation to another corresponds to an alteration of the angle θ. This can only be brought about by the application of a magnetic field H_1 in a direction at right angles to the main field H_0. Furthermore, if this new field H_1, is to be continuously effective it must rotate in a plane at right angles to the direction of H_0 in phase with the precessing nucleus. When these conditions are met the rotating magnetic field and the precessing nuclear magnet are said to be in resonance and absorption of energy by the latter can occur. The important point to be derived from the classical model at this stage is that in order to obtain a physically observable effect it is necessary to place the nucleus in a static field and then to subject it to electromagnetic radiation in such a way that the magnetic vector component of the radiation rotates with the appropriate angular velocity in a plane perpendicular to the direction of the static field. A discussion of the way in which this is achieved in practice is deferred to the next chapter which deals with the experimental procedure.

2.2 RELAXATION PROCESSES

We have now to enquire into the fate of the energy which has been absorbed by our nuclear magnet. Radiation theory tells us that the emission of energy in the form of electromagnetic radiation can take place either spontaneously or by a process stimulated by an electromagnetic field, and that the probability of occurrence of the latter process is exactly equal to the probability of absorption of energy from the field. Furthermore, the theory shows that the probability of spontaneous emission depends on the frequency of the emitted radiation in such a way that, at radiofrequencies, this probability is negligible. If we now consider a collection of nuclei of the same isotope which are equally divided between two adjacent spin states, we may conclude that the rate of absorption of energy by the lower state will exactly equal the rate of induced emission from the upper state and no observable effect is possible. The situation is saved by the fact that a collection of nuclei in a static magnetic field are not equally distributed between the various possible spin states but rather they take up a Boltzmann distribution with a very small but finite excess in favour of the lower levels. In other words the nuclei ($I = \frac{1}{2}$) all prefer to be aligned parallel to the main field (as they would be at equilibrium at $0°K$) but because of their thermal motions the best that can be managed is a slight excess of parallel spins at any instant. Small though this excess is, it is sufficient to result in a net observable absorption of radiofrequency radiation since the probability of an upward transition (absorption) is now slightly greater than that of a downward transition (emission).

Let us anticipate the subject matter of the next chapter by assuming that we have a means of detecting the absorption of radiofrequency radiation. If now we irradiate the collection of nuclei ($I = \frac{1}{2}$) the rate of absorption is initially greater than the rate of emission because of the slight excess of nuclei in the lower energy

*We may note that ω_0 is *independent* of the angle θ.

state. As a result the original excess in the lower state steadily dwindles until the two states are equally populated. If we are observing an absorption signal we might find that this signal is strong when the radiofrequency radiation is first applied but that it gradually disappears. This type of behaviour is in fact sometimes observed in practice. More generally, however, the absorption peak or signal rapidly settles down to some finite value which is invariant with time. The reason for this behaviour is that induced emission is not the only mechanism by which a nucleus can return from the upper to the lower state. There exist various possibilities for radiationless transitions by means of which the nuclei can exchange energy with their environment and it can be shown[2] that such transitions are more likely to occur from an upper to a lower state than in the reverse direction. We therefore have the situation in which the applied radiofrequency field is trying to equalize the spin state equilibrium while radiationless transitions are counteracting this process. In the type of systems of interest to the organic chemist a steady state is usually reached such that the original Boltzmann excess of nuclei in the lower states is somewhat decreased but not to zero so that a net absorption can still be registered.

The various types of radiationless transitions, by means of which a nucleus in an upper spin state returns to a lower state, are called relaxation processes. Relaxation processes are of paramount importance in the theory of nuclear magnetic resonance for not only are they responsible for the establishment and maintenance of the absorption condition but they also control the lifetime expectancy of a given state. The uncertainty principle tells us that the "natural" width of a spectral line is proportional to the reciprocal of the average time the system spends in the excited state. In ultraviolet and infrared spectroscopy, the natural line width is seldom if ever, the limit of resolution. At radiofrequencies, however, it is quite possible to reach the natural line width and we shall therefore be very much concerned with the relaxation processes which determine this parameter.

We may divide relaxation processes into two categories namely spin–lattice relaxation and spin–spin relaxation. In the latter process a nucleus in its upper state transfers its energy to a neighbouring nucleus of the same isotope by a mutual exchange of spin. This relaxation process therefore does nothing to offset the equalizing of the spin state populations caused by radiofrequency absorption and is not directly responsible for maintaining the absorption condition. In spin–lattice relaxation the energy of the nuclear spin system is converted into thermal energy of the molecular system containing the magnetic nuclei, and is therefore directly responsible for maintaining the unequal distribution of spin states. Either or both processes may control the natural line width.

Spin–lattice relaxation is sometimes called longitudinal relaxation.[3] The term *lattice* requires definition. The magnetic nuclei are usually part of an assembly of molecules which constitute a sample under investigation and the entire molecular system is referred to as the lattice irrespective of the physical state of the sample. For the moment we will confine our attention to liquids and gases in which the atoms and molecules constituting the lattice will be undergoing random translational and rotational motion. Since some or all of these atoms and molecules contain the magnetic nuclei such motions will be associated with fluctuating magnetic fields. Now, any given magnetic nucleus will be precessing about the direction of the applied field H_0 and at the same time it will experience the fluctuating magnetic fields associated with nearby lattice components. The fluctuating lattice fields can be regarded as being built up of a number of oscillating components (in the same way as any complicated wave-form may be built up from combinations of simple harmonic wave-forms) so that there will be a component which will just match the precessional frequency of the magnetic nuclei. In other words, the lattice motions, by virtue of the magnetic nuclei contained in the lattice, can from time to time generate in the neighbourhood of a nucleus in an excited spin state a field which, like the applied radiofrequency field H_1, is correctly oriented and phased to induce spin state transitions. In these circumstances a nucleus in an upper spin state can relax to the lower state and the energy lost is given to the lattice as extra translational or rotational energy. The same process is responsible for producing the Boltzmann excess of nuclei in lower states when the sample is first placed in the magnetic field. Since the exchange of energy between nuclei and lattice leaves the total energy of the sample unchanged it follows that the process must always operate so as to establish the most probable distribution of energy or, in other words, so as to establish the Boltzmann excess of nuclei in lower states.

The efficiency of spin–lattice relaxation can, like other exponential processes, be expressed in terms of a characteristic "relaxation" time T_1 which, in effect, is the half-life required for a perturbed system of nuclei to reach an equilibrium condition. A large value of T_1 indicates an inefficient relaxation process. The value of T_1 will depend on the gyromagnetic ratio (or ratios) of the nuclei in the lattice and on the nature and rapidity of the molecular motions which produce the fluctuating fields. Because of the great restriction of molecular motions in the crystal lattice, most highly purified solids exhibit very long spin–lattice relaxation times, often of the order of hours. For liquids and gases the value of T_1 is much less, being of the order of one second for many organic liquids. We shall presently discuss certain conditions under which T_1 falls to even lower values.

The term spin–spin relaxation, sometimes called transverse relaxation,[3] usually embraces two processes which result in the broadening of resonance lines. One of these processes is a true relaxation in that it shortens the life of a nucleus in any one spin state, whereas the other process broadens a resonance line by causing the effective static field to vary from nucleus to nucleus. Both effects are best understood from a consideration of the interaction of two precessing nuclear magnets in close proximity to one another. The field associated with a nuclear magnet which is precessing about the direction of the main field may be resolved into two components (Fig. 2.2). One component is static and parallel to the direction of the main field, H_0. The other component is rotating at the precessional frequency in a plane at right angles to the main field. The first component will be felt by a neighbouring nucleus as a small variation of the main field. As the individual nuclei in a system are not necessarily in the same environment, each may experience a slightly different local field due to neighbouring nuclei. Consequently, there will be a spread in the value of the resonance frequency which is, of course, proportional to the sum of the main field (H_0) and local fields. The resonance line will therefore be correspondingly broad. The rotating component at right angles to H_0 constitutes just the correct type of magnetic field for stimulating a transition in a neighbouring nucleus provided it is precessing with the same frequency. Thus there can be a mutual exchange of spin energy between the two nuclei if they are in different spin states. We have already seen that this limiting of the lifetime in any one spin state can also cause line broadening. Both these line broadening processes are usually considered together and are characterized by the spin–spin relaxation time T_2 corresponding to that average time spent in a given spin state which will result in the observed line width. We should also include a contribution from the inhomogeneity of the static magnetic field H_0 since, if the field varies from point to point over the region which is to be occupied by the sample, a spreading of the precessional frequency will result.

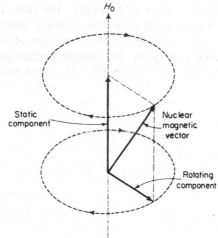

FIG. 2.2 The resolution of the magnetic vector of a nucleus into a static and a rotating component.

A consideration of the two relaxation processes corresponding to T_1 and T_2 enables us to predict what effect the physical state of a substance will have on the observed absorption line. Many solids may be considered as more or less rigid assemblages of nuclei in which random movement of the lattice components is negligible. For this reason spin–lattice relaxation times may be very long. On the other hand, local fields associated with spin–spin interaction are large and result in low values of T_2 with the result that absorption lines of solids are usually very broad. In fact, the broadening in solids is usually several powers of ten greater than the effects which are of interest to the organic chemist and for this reason we will consider solids no further. In liquids, molecules may undergo random motion (Brownian movement) and it can be shown[4] that, provided this motion is sufficiently rapid, the local fields average out to a very small value, so that sharp resonance lines can be observed. Indeed, with liquids, other factors including the spin–lattice relaxation are of comparable importance in determining line width. A further consequence of random motion in liquids is a marked lowering of the spin–lattice relaxation time, T_1. The observed value of T_1 depends amongst other things on the viscosity of the liquid. The dependence is not a simple one but assumes the form indicated in Fig. 2.3.

The origin of this behaviour can be understood in terms of the fluctuating fields which effect the relaxation. At high viscosities the molecular motions are relatively slow and the fluctuating fields are largely built up of lower frequency components so that the intensity of the component ν_0, which matches the precessional frequency

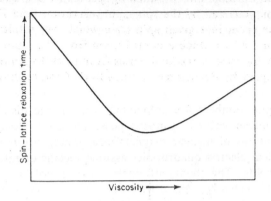

FIG. 2.3   The dependence of the spin–lattice relaxation time on viscosity.

of the magnetic nuclei and causes relaxation, will be relatively low. On the other hand the fluctuating fields in a very mobile liquid are comprised of a large range of frequencies so that any one frequency (in particular ν_0) makes only a small contribution. Evidently some intermediate viscosity will provide the maximum intensity of the correct frequency ν_0 (see Fig. 2.4) and hence the minimum value of T_1. In addition to the effect of viscosity on T_1, we should note that at very high

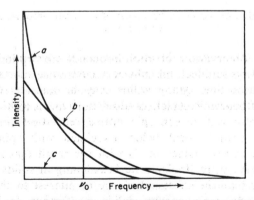

FIG. 2.4   The variation of the frequency distribution of fluctuating molecular magnetic fields with viscosity (a) high viscosity; (b) intermediate viscosity; (c) low viscosity.

viscosities it is possible that the molecules are moving about too slowly to effect complete time-averaging of local fields, so that, even though T_1 is long, T_2 becomes short and broadened lines are observed.

We need to know about two special types of spin–lattice relaxation which sometimes influence our observations. The first of these may be termed para-magnetic broadening and results from the presence of paramagnetic molecules or ions in the sample under investigation. The electron magnetic moment is some 10^3 times larger than nuclear magnetic moments. Consequently the motions of paramagnetic lattice components will produce very intense fluctuating magnetic fields and greatly reduced spin–lattice relaxation times, T_1, result. Under these conditions T_1 makes a large contribution to line width and the nuclear magnetic resonance lines of paramagnetic substances are very broad. Furthermore, the presence of even small quantities of paramagnetic impurities in a sample can cause line-broadening.

The second special type of spin–lattice relaxation concerns those nuclei which possess an electric quadrupole moment. We have seen (p. 2) that nuclei with spin numbers I equal to one-half have a spherically symmetrical charge distribution, whereas higher spin numbers are associated with charge distributions of lower symmetry so that nuclei with $I > \frac{1}{2}$ mostly possess an electric quadrupole moment. Just as the orientations of nuclear magnets in a homogeneous magnetic field are quantized, so nuclear electric quadrupoles assume specific orientations in inhomogeneous electric fields. The theory of nuclear quadrupole resonance is really a separate branch of spectroscopy[5] and we need only consider here the way in which nuclear quadrupoles provide an additional mode of relaxation. Polar molecules in motion produce fluctuating local electrostatic field gradients. A nucleus $(I > \frac{1}{2})$ in an excited spin state, by virtue of the interaction of its quadrupole with fluctuating field gradients, is thus offered an additional method of giving up its spin energy to the lattice. The essential feature of the electric interaction is that it is usually stronger and falls off less rapidly with distance than its magnetic counterpart which persists only over a very short distance (< 4 Å). Consequently nuclei with quadrupole moments frequently exhibit very short spin–lattice relaxation times and the observed absorption lines associated with these nuclei are correspondingly broad.

2.3 SATURATION

We have seen that adequate spin–lattice relaxation is a necessary condition for the continued observation of radiofrequency absorption. In practice this condition is not always fulfilled and in such circumstances the observed absorption signal diminishes with time and may, in extreme cases, vanish. The preceding development of the theory of relaxation is sufficient for us to be able to understand this behaviour which is called *saturation*. Considering nuclei with $I = \frac{1}{2}$, we have seen that the static magnetic field H_0 establishes a small excess (n_0) of nuclei in the lower spin state and that the absorption of radiofrequency power tends to reduce this excess. As there is competition between the absorption process and spin-lattice relaxation a new steady value (n_s) for the excess of nuclei in the lower spin state, is obtained. The value of n_s may range between n_0 and zero. If $n_s = n_0$ the absorption condition will be maintained at its original level whereas if $n_s = 0$ the absorption of radiofrequency power will cease. Between these two extremes we have the situation where the absorption starts at some value and rapidly falls to a lower value. The ratio $n_s/n_0 = Z_0$ is known as the saturation factor and is of course a direct measure of the degree to which the absorption condition is maintained. It can be shown that for $I = \frac{1}{2}$ the saturation factor is given by equation (4).[1,2,3] We note that low values of Z_0 correspond to a high degree of saturation.

$$Z_0 = [1 + \gamma^2 H_1^2 T_1 T_2]^{-1}$$

Equation (4) tells us the conditions under which we may expect appreciable saturation. Firstly, the inclusion of the term H_1^2 expresses the self-evident conclusion that the greater the radiofrequency power applied to the sample the greater will be the degree of saturation. The term T_2 takes into account the width of the absorption line. A narrow absorption line corresponds to a high proportion of nuclei with precessional frequencies exactly equal to the applied radiofrequency field. Thus, taken together, $\gamma^2 . H_1^2 . T_2$ expresses the probability of radiofrequency induced transitions. The term T_1 is an inverse measure of the probability of spin–lattice transitions. Therefore a combination of large radiofrequency fields, narrow absorption lines and long spin–lattice relaxation times may prevent the observation of a spectrum. Furthermore, when saturation is appreciable it is those nuclei with exactly the correct precessional frequency which are lost from the excess, n_0, so that the new excess (n_s) will correspond to a broader resonance line. The strength of an observed resonance signal from a given type of nucleus is a function both of the radiofrequency power H_1 and of the concentration of those nuclei in the sample, so that the saturation factor Z_0 ultimately determines the minimum concentration which will give an observable spectrum (see next chapter).

2.4   MAGNETIC SHIELDING OF ATOMIC NUCLEI

So far in our discussion of nuclear magnetic resonance we have more or less assumed that the resonance frequency of a nucleus is simply a function of the applied field and the gyromagnetic ratio of the nucleus. If this were indeed the case nuclear magnetic resonance would be of little value to the organic chemist. It turns out, however, that the resonance frequency is to a small degree dependent on its molecular environment. This is because the extranuclear electrons magnetically screen the nucleus so that the magnetic field felt by the nucleus is not quite the same as the applied field. Naturally, we might expect the efficiency of this shielding by the extranuclear electrons to bear some sort of relationship to the type of chemical bonding involved. Thus naïvely we might predict that electron withdrawal from a given nucleus would decrease the shielding of that nucleus. To the extent to which this is true we can regard the magnetic nucleus as a tiny probe with which we may examine the surrounding electron distribution. Although, as we shall see presently, the nuclear resonance picture of electron distribution is not nearly as simple as the one drawn above it has been found that nuclear resonance frequencies, when properly determined, are remarkably characteristic of molecular structure. The empirical approach developed in subsequent chapters shows that nuclear resonance spectroscopy is a technique equal in value to the other powerful physico-chemical aids for the determination of organic structures.

We shall be principally concerned with the nuclear magnetic resonance of the hydrogen nucleus, that is with proton magnetic resonance, and a preliminary idea of the effect of structure on proton resonance frequencies can be gained by reference to Fig. 2.5. We see that protons in the usual types of organic environments have relative frequencies spread over about 400 cycles per second (c/s) at a field strength of 9365 gauss for which resonance frequency of the hydrogen nucleus $\nu_H = 40 \times 10^6$ c/s. Although this spread is only equivalent to about ten parts per million, *relative* values for proton signals can be readily determined with an accuracy of ± 1 c/s. The separation of resonance frequencies of nuclei in different structural environments from some arbitrarily chosen line position is generally termed the *chemical shift*. If the arbitrary line position is that of a bare proton the chemical shift is equal to the screening constant which measures the difference between the applied field and the actual field felt by the nucleus. The chemical shifts of protons are amongst the smallest for all nuclei but, as both carbon (^{12}C) and oxygen (^{16}O) do not possess magnetic moments, the major application of nuclear magnetic resonance spectroscopy to organic chemistry involves the study of proton shifts.

Although our approach to the subject is to be largely empirical we will find it useful to enquire a little more deeply into the origins of the chemical shift, for some of the theoretical findings do permit qualitative predictions which are of value in structural work. Much of the necessary theoretical background for an understanding of chemical shifts was developed much earlier as part of the theory of diamagnetic susceptibilities. The explicit extension to nuclear resonance is largely due to Ramsey[6,7,8,9] and Pople.[10,11,12] For the most part we will follow Pople's treatment.

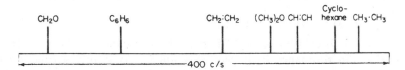

FIG. 2.5 Chemical shifts of protons in different environments (determined at 40 Mc).

We begin our discussion by noting that, in the absence of a magnetic field, the majority of molecules which are studied by organic chemists do not possess a resultant electron spin (i.e. they are not free radicals) so that electron spin does not make a direct contribution to shielding. Electronic shielding arises from circulation of electrons about a nucleus. These circulations are induced by the applied magnetic field. Let us consider the case of an atom for which the electron distribution is necessarily spherically symmetrical. Here we may visualize the shielding process in the following way: in a uniform magnetic field the electrons will be caused to circulate about the nucleus in such a direction as to produce a secondary magnetic field which, in the region of the nucleus, is opposed to the applied field.* In other words, the circulation of electrons induced by the applied field corresponds to a current passing around a circular loop in a plane at right angles to the applied field (Fig. 2.6). This loop constitutes a solenoid in which the direction of the current is such that the associated magnetic field at the centre of the loop is opposed to the applied field. The nucleus experiences the effect of both the applied and the induced field and the resultant field is therefore less than the applied field. It is important to note that the strength of the induced field is proportional to the strength of the applied field.

---

*The motion imposed on atomic electrons by a uniform magnetic field is known as Larmor precession. The nature and frequency of this precessional motion are stated in Larmor's theorem, a proof of which has been given by Van Vleck (*The Theory of Electric and Magnetic Susceptibilities*, Oxford University Press, 1932, p. 22). It is sufficient for our purpose to realize that such circulations do occur and that the precessional frequency and hence the induced magnetic field are proportional to the strength of the uniform field.

An extension of the simple atomic model to the molecular problem is not possible because the spherical symmetry is lost and the electron circulations no longer follow simple paths. Pople[10,11] has developed a quantum mechanical treatment of the induced electron circulations in molecules in which he separates the electron motions into three components. The separation, *which is quite arbitrary,* is made for mathematical convenience but the procedure provides a useful model for qualitative discussion. The three types of electron circulations are (a) local diamagnetic currents, (b) paramagnetic currents, and (c) interatomic diamagnetic currents.

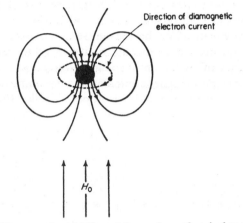

Direction of diamagnetic
electron current

H_0

Fig. 2.6   Diamagnetic shielding of the nucleus of an isolated atom.

Local diamagnetic currents correspond to the atomic case discussed above. The electron distribution about the nucleus is considered to be spherically symmetrical since the effects of departure from this symmetry are allowed for later by the consideration of the other two types of circulations. Local diamagnetic currents therefore provide a source of *positive* shielding; that is they reduce the total field experienced by the nucleus. The only way in which molecular environment can affect the local diamagnetic shielding is by an alteration of the electron density around the nucleus concerned. Thus we may predict on the basis of the inductive effect of Robinson and Ingold that the shielding and hence the resonance

frequencies of the protons in the series $CH_3 . C\!\!\!<$, $CH_3 . N\!\!\!<$, $CH_3 . O\!\!-$ should

decrease from left to right provided that the local diamagnetic shielding contribution is dominant. It can be shown for molecules in the liquid and gaseous states that the field arising from local diamagnetic circulations about one nucleus makes *no* contribution to the shielding of a neighbouring nucleus.*

In terms of local diamagnetic currents the position of the aldehydic proton corresponds to the removal of half an electron from the carbon-hydrogen bond. It is clear that in this example some other effect is operative. Similarly the frequencies of the protons in ethane, ethylene, and acetylene (Fig. 2.5) bear no

*This point is explained with the aid of a diagram in Chapter 7.

relation to the known "acidities" of these compounds. In these systems, para-magnetic currents make a significant contribution to the shielding of the protons. The paramagnetic shielding term* (and also the interatomic diamagnetic term discussed below) allows for the fact that the ease with which electrons in a *molecule* circulate depends on the orientation of the molecule with respect to the main field or, in other words, it corrects for the diamagnetic anisotropy of the electronic environment of a nucleus in a molecule. Paramagnetic circulations of electrons about a nucleus produce a secondary magnetic field parallel to the applied field at the nucleus so that the shielding of the nucleus is decreased. Mathematically, the paramagnetic shielding term corresponds to a mixing, under the influence of the applied field, of the ground state electronic configuration with low lying excited states of the correct symmetry. For this reason we do not expect *local* paramagnetic circulations about a proton to contribute to its shielding because the available electronic excited states of hydrogen are energetically too high to participate in mixing. However, local paramagnetic circulations are important in the shielding of nuclei other than hydrogen and its isotopes. Unlike the local diamagnetic circulations, paramagnetic circulations about one nucleus may contribute to the shielding of a neighbouring nucleus so that electrons associated with nuclei such as carbon, oxygen, nitrogen, etc., sometimes play an important role in determining the shielding of near-by protons, and it is this type of effect which accounts for the anomalous proton frequency of acetylene relative to ethane and ethylene, and also for the greatly reduced shielding of aldehydic protons.

Pople[10,11] has made a theoretical study of acetylene and has shown that para-magnetic currents are induced at the carbon atoms by the component of the applied field which is perpendicular to the molecular axis. The fields associated with such circulations are equivalent to those of tiny bar magnets placed at each carbon atom. By referring to Fig. 2.7A we can see that, whereas these fields are paramagnetic at the carbon nuclei, they are diamagnetic at the protons and hence they augment the shielding of the protons. Since the paramagnetic term arises because the magnetically induced motions of the electrons are restricted in certain directions we should be able to account for the abnormal shielding of acetylenic protons by considering the diamagnetic anisotropy of the triple bond. This we may do intuitively, for it is readily apparent (Fig. 2.7B) that if the direction of the applied field is coincident with the molecular axis the π-electrons can circulate within the π-orbitals which in the case of acetylene are axially symmetric. This diamagnetic circulation shields the protons. If the field is perpendicular to the molecular axis no convenient circular paths can be envisaged. Thus, the para-magnetic currents in Pople's treatment merely express reduced diamagnetic polar-izability perpendicular to the triple bond.

According to Pople,[11] paramagnetic circulations at the carbon and oxygen atoms of an aldehyde carbonyl group occur when the direction of the applied field is in the plane of the trigonal carbon atom. This is equivalent to saying that the diamagnetic polarizability of the bond is greatest in a direction perpendicular to this plane and the induced field will therefore diminish the shielding of the alde-hydic proton. The aldehydic proton is thus much less shielded than an aliphatic

---

*Sometimes referred to as the second order paramagnetic term to distinguish it from terms arising from resultant electron spin in the ground state.

proton not only because the inductive effect of the carbonyl group reduces the local diamagnetic term but also because of the nature of the paramagnetic term. The examples provided by acetylene and an aldehyde show us that the paramagnetic term may operate in either direction dependent on molecular structure. Organic chemists will welcome further theoretical contributions which give them information, however qualitative, about the nature of the paramagnetic effect in other structures (see Chapter 7).

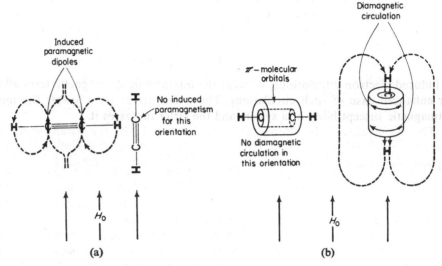

Fig. 2.7A and B   The shileding of acetylenic protons (a) explanation in terms of induced paramagnetism; (b) explanation in terms of diamagnetic anisotropy.

The two effects so far discussed deal only with electron circulations confined to the immediate vicinity of one particular atom. It is known that certain structures permit the circulation of electrons over a number of atomic centres and when this can occur an additional shielding mechanism is available. Diamagnetic currents of this type are most readily developed in large closed loops such as provided by the π-electron system of benzene. This is depicted in Fig. 2.8. The mechanics are similar to the diamagnetic shielding of atoms (p. 15) except that now we are not so interested in the field at the centre of the "solenoid" but rather with the region outside the current ring in which the aromatic protons are situated. We see in Fig. 2.8 that the induced field at the aromatic protons is parallel to the main field and hence these protons are deshielded by the interatomic diamagnetic term. The concept of ring currents is one which lends itself to direct calculation of the interatomic diamagnetic term and several approximate methods have been developed.[13,14,15,16,17,18] Furthermore, the model predicts that protons occupying positions on or near the six-fold axis of the benzene ring experience the diamagnetic part of the induced field and accordingly should be shielded by the interatomic diamagnetic effect. This situation is encountered in the polymethylenebenzene (I) in which the two central methylene groups are found to be abnormally shielded.[15] Interatomic diamagnetic circulations are believed to be responsible for the diamagnetic anisotropy of certain single bonds (see Chapter 7).

Both paramagnetic and interatomic diamagnetic terms may contribute to the diamagnetic anisotropy of a chemical group and we shall sometimes refer to a shielding effect as arising from the diamagnetic anisotropy of a group without explicitly stating the cause of the anisotropy. The essential difference between the two terms lies in the fact that the paramagnetic term corrects for the restriction

I

of induced electron circulations, whereas the interatomic diamagnetic term allows for enhanced ease of such circulations. Thus, the former term lowers the molar diamagnetic susceptibility of a system and the latter increases it.

The magnitudes of the electron currents associated with the paramagnetic and interatomic effects vary with the instantaneous orientation of the molecule in the applied field, and the observed effect is the average over all orientations.

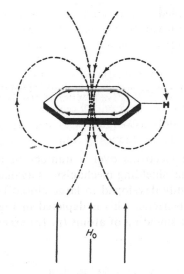

FIG. 2.8   The shielding of aromatic protons.

All three shielding mechanisms are the result of induced currents which are proportional to the applied field. We therefore draw the important conclusion, which is accurately borne out by experiment, that *the frequency of the chemical shift is directly proportional to the strength of the applied field.* Thus, with high enough applied fields and in favourable cases, we may hope to observe a separate line or band for each equivalent* group of protons in a molecule. Since, in the final analysis, exactly the same transition is involved for each and every proton

*By "equivalent" we mean that the protons have the same chemical shift.

(namely, the turning over of the proton magnet in the field) the intensities of the bands, as given by the areas which they enclose, will be in the ratio of the number of protons in each group. Therefore, to a first approximation, the spectrum of ethanol will consist of three chemically shifted bands with intensities in the ratio of 3 : 2 : 1, arising from the methyl, methylene, and hydroxyl protons respectively. The low resolution spectrum of ethanol (Fig. 2.9) is in accord with this prediction.

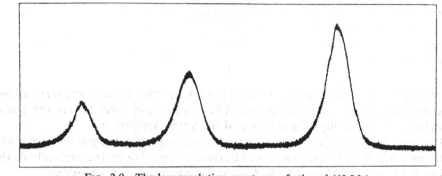

FIG. 2.9   The low resolution spectrum of ethanol (40 Mc).

We have so far confined our discussion mainly to proton chemical shifts. Other nuclei possessing nuclear moments also exhibit chemical shifts which are usually much larger than those observed for protons.

2.5   ELECTRON COUPLED SPIN–SPIN INTERACTIONS

If we examine a sample of ordinary ethanol (not highly purified) under higher resolution than that used to obtain Fig. 2.9 we find a somewhat more complicated picture (Fig. 2.10). The bands associated with the methyl and methylene groups now appear as multiplets the total areas of which are still in the ratio of 3 : 2. The

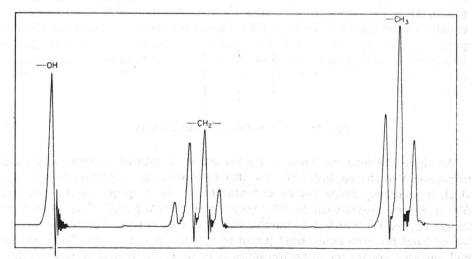

FIG. 2.10   The high resolution spectrum of ethanol obtained at 40 Mc with a sample containing a trace of acid.

spacing of the three components of the methyl group triplet are found to be exactly equal to that in the quartet from the methylene groups. Furthermore the areas of the components of each multiplet approximate to simple integral ratios (e.g. 1 : 2 : 1 for the triplet and 1 : 3 : 3 : 1 for the quartet). We can understand these observations if we imagine that the field experienced by the protons of one group is influenced by the spins of protons in the neighbouring group. Let us consider the methyl protons in relation to the possible spin arrangements of the two methylene protons. There are four possible spin arrangements for the methylene group. If we label the two protons A and B then we have (1) A+B both in parallel spin states, (2) A+B both in antiparallel spin states, (3) A parallel and B antiparallel, and (4) A antiparallel and B parallel. The arrangements (3) and (4) are clearly equiv-

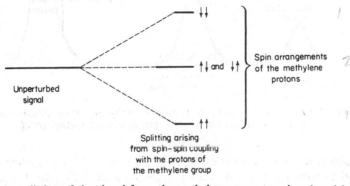

FIG. 2.11 The splitting of the signal from the methyl group protons in ethanol by spin–spin interaction with the protons of the methylene group.

alent. The magnetic effect of these arrangements is in some way (see below) transmitted to the methyl group protons so that these protons will feel one of three effective fields according to the instantaneous spin arrangement of the methylene group. Thus, for a collection of ethanol molecules there will therefore be three equally spaced transition energies (frequencies) for the methyl protons. Since the probabilities of existence of each of the four spin arrangements are equal and taking into account the fact that (3) and (4) are equivalent it follows that the intensities of the three transitions will be 1 : 2 : 1. These results are illustrated schematically in Fig. 2.11. Similarly we find that the spins of the methyl group can be arranged in eight ways of which there are two sets of three equivalent arrangements (Fig. 2.12) thus accounting for the observed structure of the methylene multiplet. The lack of multiplicity of the hydroxyl proton signal and further splitting of the methylene group signal has an explanation which is dealt with in the last section of this chapter.

Now, we have already considered spin–spin interactions (p. 10) and have noted that, while local fields are possible in solids, in liquids they are almost completely averaged to zero by rapid molecular motions. In order to explain the present observations we must have an interaction mechanism which does not depend on the direct transmission of the magnetic field through space. An explanation which has been advanced by Ramsey[19] is that the bonding electrons are responsible for letting one nucleus know the spin state of a neighbouring nucleus. Let us consider a hypothetical single covalent bond between two atoms, A and B ($I_A = I_B = \frac{1}{2}$) and let us denote parallel and antiparallel spin states, whether they be of nuclei or electrons, by α and β respectively. It is known, from the way in which the two electrons of the covalent bond correlate, that at any instant there is a high probability of finding one electron in the immediate vicinity of nucleus A and the other

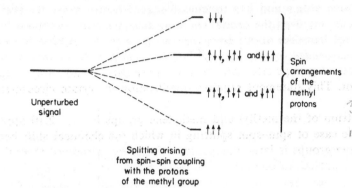

FIG. 2.12   The splitting of the signal from the methylene group protons in ethanol by spin–spin interaction with the protons of the methyl group.

in the neighbourhood of nucleus B. It is also known that nuclear and electron spins tend to pair, i.e. when they are closely associated they tend to have opposite spins. Therefore, if nucleus B has an α spin the spin of the electron in its vicinity will most frequently be β. Therefore, by the Pauli principle, the electron in the neighbourhood of A must most frequently have an α spin. Because of this the energy of the β spin state of A is lowered and that of the α state is raised. In this way the spin of nucleus B influences the transition energies of nucleus A as is shown diagramatically in Fig. 2.13.

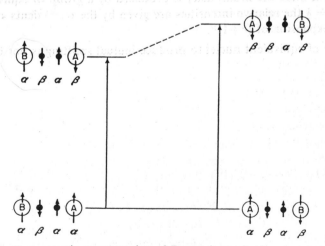

FIG. 2.13   A diagrammatic representation of Ramsey's mechanism for electron coupled spin–spin interaction.

An alternative explanation put forward by Gutowsky and his co-workers[20] is that orbital motions (i.e. induced electron circulations) may so shield the direct interaction between nuclei that the local fields constituting this interaction might not be averaged to zero by molecular motions. Direct calculations have shown that, for protons, Ramsey's mechanism is the predominant one. More recently, Pople[21] has examined the contribution of orbital coupling (Gutowsky's mechanism) between fluorine atoms and has concluded that if highly polar (in the electrical sense) bonds are involved the orbital coupling mechanism is significant.

It is evident from the above mechanisms that *electron coupled spin–spin inter-actions are independent of the strength of the applied field* so that although the chemical shifts of groups alter with field strength the spacing of spin–spin multiplets does not. This statement requires qualification in certain circumstances (see pp. 24, 88).

The spectrum of the methyl and methylene groups in Fig. 2.10 approximates to an extreme case of spin–spin splitting in which the chemical shift between the two interacting groups is large compared with the magnitude of the splitting and in which each nucleus in one group interacts equally with each and every nucleus in the second group. When these two conditions are met the multiplet structure is governed by a very simple set of rules.

(1) The nuclei of an equivalent group (e.g. the three protons of the methyl group in ethanol) do not interact with each other in such a way as to cause observable multiplicity.

(2) The multiplicity of the band arising from a group of equivalent nuclei is determined by the neighbouring groups of equivalent nuclei. A neighbouring group of equivalent nuclei causes a multiplicity which is given by the formula $(2nI+1)$ where n is the number of equivalent nuclei of spin I in that group. If there are more than two interacting groups the multiplicity of one (A) is given by $(2n_B I_B+1)(2n_C I_C+1)\ldots$

(3) The intensities of a multiplet are symmetric about the mid-point of the band and when the multiplicity is produced by a group of equivalent nuclei with $I = \frac{1}{2}$ the relative intensities are given by the coefficients of the terms in the expansion of $(r+1)^n$.

The failure of equivalent nuclei to produce mutual splitting is not because they do not interact with one another but because transitions between the states produced by such interactions are forbidden by the appropriate selection rules. A detailed analysis of this problem has been given by Hahn and Maxwell.[22] In cases where the chemical shift between two groups is large compared with the multiplet spacing, the separations of adjacent components in a multiplet will be equal to each other and to the separation of the components in the multiplet arising from the second group involved in the mutual splitting. The separations 1–2, 2–3, 4–5, 5–6 and 6–7* in the ethanol spectrum (Fig. 2.10) are all equal. This separation is a direct measure of the effectiveness of the electron coupled spin–spin interaction and is known as the coupling constant, J. J is independent of field strength. Its magnitude is dependent on the gyromagnetic ratio of the nuclei and on the structural relationship of the groups involved. We do not expect coupling between widely separated

* Labelling the peaks from right to left.

groups in a molecule as there is little chance of electron exchange between them. Usually, coupling only occurs across one, two, or three bonds although it can and does extend further in systems with delocalized electronic structures such as conjugated systems and certain small ring compounds. There is as yet no adequate theory which accounts for the magnitude of J in terms of structure but there is evidence that the steric relationship of groups is important (Chapter 6).

It is possible to have two equivalent groups of nuclei in which a nucleus in one group is not equally coupled to each nucleus in the second group. 1 : 1-Difluoro-ethylene (II) provides an example of this situation since in this molecule there are

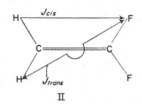

II

obviously two types of interactions, *cis* and *trans*, which are not necessarily equal.[23] The simple splitting rules are no longer obeyed and the proton spectrum of this molecule is shown in Fig. 2.14. Spectra of this type are discussed in Chapter 6. Free rotation of the methyl group in ethanol insures that there is only one coupling constant between the methylene and methyl protons.

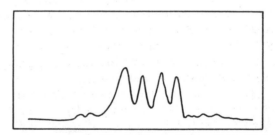

FIG. 2.14   The proton spectrum of 1 : 1-difluoroethylene (After H. M. McConnell[23]).

When we turn to interacting groups of nuclei for which the coupling constant J is of the same order as the chemical shift between the groups we find that the multiplicity rules given above no longer hold. Usually, more lines appear and simple patterns of spacings and intensities are no longer found. Indeed, if we look at the spectrum of ethanol under high resolution and at not too high a field, we can just see (Fig. 2.15) the fine structure known as second order splitting which arises in this way. Figure 2.16 shows the theoretical spectrum of a nuclear system of three interacting protons, ($H_A H_A H_B$), two of which are equivalent. When the chemical shift between the pair of protons ($H_A H_A$), and the remaining proton, (H_B), is large compared with the coupling constant, J_{AB}, the spectrum is given by the rules on p. 23. When the chemical shift is zero the spectrum degenerates to a single line. Intermediate situations give rise to complicated nine line spectra. Mathematical techniques have been developed for computing the theoretical spectra for various nuclear systems in cases where coupling constants and chemical shifts are of the same order. We shall return to this problem in Chapter 6 and leading references will be given there.

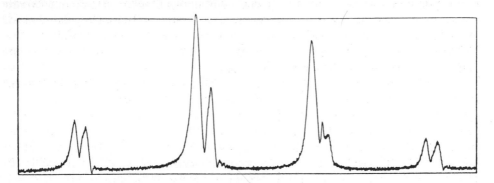

Fig. 2.15   The methylene band of ethanol under very high resolution at 40 Mc.

In order that spin–spin splitting may be observed it is necessary that the nuclei responsible for the splitting should spend a time in a given spin state arrangement which is long in comparison with the reciprocal of the frequency separation of the multiplet components.[20] If the spin arrangements of the group are changing with a frequency which is much greater than the coupling constant J (in cycles per second), then the neighbouring group undergoing a transition experiences a field

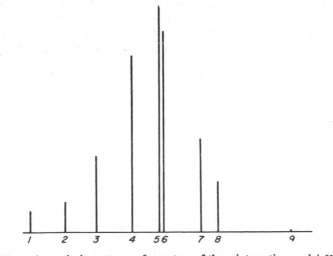

Fig. 2.16   A theoretical spectrum of a system of three interacting nuclei $H_A H_A H_B$.

which is the average of the various spin arrangements, and a single absorption-line results. This state of affairs can be brought about artificially in certain molecules by a technique known as spin decoupling or double resonance. If, for instance, we are observing a proton absorption line which is split as a doublet by a neighbouring phosphorus nucleus ($I = \frac{1}{2}$) we can reduce the lifetime of the phosphorus nucleus in any one spin state by irradiating the sample at a frequency equal to the resonance frequency of phosphorus and so remove the splitting of the proton line. As the resonance frequency of phosphorus lies well below that of the proton this procedure will not interfere with our experiment. The double resonance technique is potentially a very valuable aid in the analysis of complex spectra but as yet few examples of its use have been reported. One example of the spin decoupling of mutually interacting protons has been reported[24] and the development of this technique into a routine procedure would constitute a major advance in nuclear magnetic resonance spectroscopy.

Partial or complete spin decoupling is often associated with nuclei possessing electric quadrupole moments because the lifetimes of such nuclei in any particular spin state are limited by rapid spin–lattice relaxation (p. 9). For this reason signals from protons attached to nuclei such as nitrogen ($I > \frac{1}{2}$) may not exhibit the expected spin–spin splitting but instead may consist of very broad bands corresponding to partial averaging of the coupling. In such cases it is possible to produce sharp signals by using the double resonance technique to complete the spin decoupling. An example of this procedure will be discussed in Chapter 5. Pople[25] has derived theoretical band shapes associated with various spin–lattice relaxation times.

2.6 CHEMICAL EXCHANGE AND HINDERED ROTATION

When we discussed the high resolution spectrum of ethanol we noted that the resonance line of the hydroxylic proton did not exhibit multiplicity although we might have expected it to be split as a triplet by spin–spin coupling with the adjacent methylenic protons. Actually if the spectrum of a highly purified specimen of ethanol is examined the expected multiplicity of the hydroxylic proton signal is observed together with an increase in the multiplicity of the band from the methylene group (Fig. 2.17). It has been found that acidic or basic impurities are responsible for the removal of the coupling between the hydroxylic and methylenic

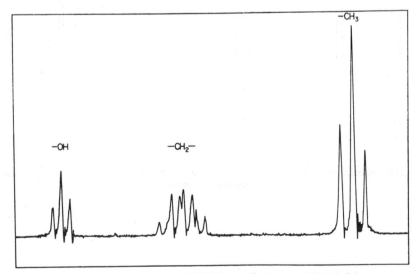

FIG. 2.17. The spectrum of highly purified ethanol (40 Mc/s.).

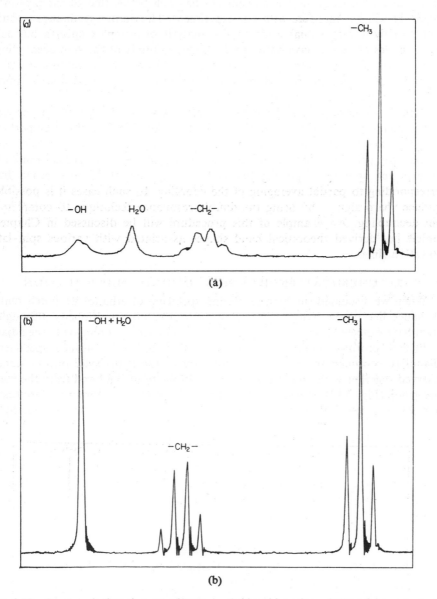

(a)

(b)

FIG. 2.18. Spectra of ethanol-water mixtures. *a* Acid and base free. *b* Containing a trace of hydrocloric acid.

protons. The explanation of this phenomenon lies in the existence of a rapid chemical exchange of hydroxylic protons which is catalysed by acids or bases. As a result of this exchange any one hydroxylic proton, during a certain interval of time, will be attached to a number of different ethanol molecules and will thus experience all possible spin arrangements of the methylene group. If the chemical exchange occurs with a frequency which is substantially greater than the frequency separation of the components of the multiplet from the hydroxylic proton, the magnetic effects corresponding to three possible spin arrangements of the methylenic protons are averaged, and a single sharp absorption line is observed. In other words, rapid chemical exchange causes spin decoupling of the hydroxylic and methylenic protons (cf. ref. 26).

Chemical exchange can also affect the chemical shifts of nuclei. To illustrate this we shall consider the behaviour of a mixture of ethanol and water. In the absence of acidic or basic catalysts the spectrum of this mixture possesses bands characteristic of the protons of water and of the hydroxylic protons of ethanol* (Fig. 2.18). If a trace of an acid or base is added to the mixture these two bands coalesce to a single sharp line. It is evident that rapid proton exchange between water and ethanol averages the shielding of each environment. The condition for the observation of a single sharp line is that the frequency of proton exchange should be much greater than the frequency separation of the two lines observed in the absence of exchange. If the frequency of exchange is of the same order as the separation of the two lines the shielding characteristic of each environment is only partially averaged and a broad band results. This region of indeterminancy can be defined quite accurately[27] and may be used to derive the rates of exchange even though such processes may have half-times of the order of a hundredth of a second. The position of the single sharp line observed when exchange is rapid will depend on the relative concentrations of the two species. Some further aspects of chemical exchange will be considered in Chapter 5.

Rotation about single bonds results in a situation which is rather similar to chemical exchange, in that signals characteristic of each conformation may or may not be observed depending on the rate of conformational interchange and on considerations of molecular asymmetry. We shall examine this problem in some detail in Chapter 6 but we may note that rotation about most single bonds is sufficiently rapid at room temperature to preclude the observation of separate signals from each conformation.

REFERENCES

1. N. BLOEMBERGEN, E. M. PURCELL and R. V. POUND, *Phys. Rev.* **73,** 679 (1948).
2. G. E. PAKE, *Am. J. Phys.* **18,** 438, 473 (1950).
3. F. BLOCK, *Phys. Rev.* **70,** 460 (1946).
4. F. BLOCK, W. W. HANSEN and M. PACKARD, *ibid,* **474.**
5. W. J. ORVILLE-THOMAS, *Quart. Rev.* **11,** 162 (1957).
6. N. F. RAMSEY, *Phys. Rev.* **78,** 699 (1950).
7. N. F. RAMSEY, *ibid.* **83,** 450 (1951).
8. N. F. RAMSEY, *ibid.* **85,** 60 (1952).
9. N. F. RAMSEY, *ibid.* **86,** 243 (1952).
10. J. A. POPLE, *Proc. Roy. Soc.* A**239,** 541 (1957).

*This is only true at room temperature if the concentration of water is comparatively low (>30 per cent v/v).

11. J. A. Pople, *ibid.* 550.
12. W. G. Schneider, H. J. Bernstein and J. A. Pople, *J. Chem. Phys.* **28,** 601 (1958).
13. H. J. Bernstein, W. G. Schneider and J. A. Pople, *Proc. Roy. Soc.* A236, 515 (1956).
14. J. A. Pople, *J. Chem. Phys.* **24,** 1111 (1956).
15. J. S. Waugh and R. W. Fessenden, *J. Am. Chem. Soc.* **79,** 846 (1957).
16. J. A. Pople, *Molecular Phys.* **1,** 175 (1958).
17. R. McWeeny, *ibid.* 311.
18. C. E. Johnson and F. A. Bovey, *J. Chem. Phys.* **29** 1012 (1958).
19. N. F. Ramsey, *Phys. Rev.* **91,** 303 (1953); N. F. Ramsay and E. M. Purcell, *ibid.* **85,** 143 (1952).
20. H. S. Gutowsky, D. W. McCall and C. P. Schichter, *J. Chem. Phys.* **21,** 279 (1953).
21. J. A. Pople, *Molecular Phys.* **1,** 216 (1958).
22. E. L. Hahn and D. E. Maxwell, *Phys. Rev.* **88,** 1070 (1952).
23. H. M. McConnell, A. D. McLean and C. A. Reilly, *J. Chem. Phys.* **23,** 1152 (1955).
24. W. A. Anderson, *Phys. Rev.* **102,** 151 (1956).
25. J. A. Pople, *Molecular Phys.* **1,** 168 (1958).
26. H. S. Gutowsky and A. Saika, *J. Chem. Phys.* **21,** 1688 (1953).
27. H. S. Gutowsky and C. H. Holm, *ibid.* **25,** 1228 (1956).

CHAPTER 3

THE EXPERIMENTAL METHOD

A HIGH resolution nuclear magnetic resonance spectrometer in its present form is an instrument of considerable complexity and a detailed knowledge of the electronic equipment will not be of any great advantage to the organic chemist. We will therefore describe the apparatus in the broadest possible terms and discuss in detail only those points of the experimental technique which lie within the operator's control and which are of importance in that they directly determine the character of the spectra obtained. Our particular concern in this chapter will be the calibration of spectra and the methods of expressing results, for, from the organic chemist's point of view, nuclear magnetic resonance is principally a new spectroscopic method which, like infrared and ultraviolet spectroscopy, provides us with numbers characteristic of atoms and their arrangements in complex molecules.

3.1 THE NUCLEAR MAGNETIC RESONANCE SPECTROMETER: A BRIEF DESCRIPTION

The apparatus consists essentially of four parts:
 (i) a magnet capable of producing a very strong homogeneous field;
 (ii) a means of continuously varying the magnetic field over a very small range;
 (iii) a radiofrequency oscillator;
 (iv) a radiofrequency receiver.

The magnet is necessary to produce the condition for the absorption of radiofrequency radiation. The remaining components then have analogues in other methods of absorption spectroscopy. Thus the radiofrequency oscillator is the source of radiant energy. The device for varying the magnetic field over a small range corresponds to a prism or grating in as much as it permits us to scan the spectrum and determine the positions of absorption lines in terms of frequency or field strength (p. 6). The radiofrequency receiver is the "detector" or device which tells us when energy from the source is being absorbed by the sample.

3.2 THE MAGNET

Both permanent and electromagnets are employed in nuclear magnetic resonance spectroscopy. The essential feature of the magnet is that it should possess a region between the pole faces in which the magnetic field is homogeneous to a high order (1 in 10^8). By homogeneous we mean that the strength and direction of the field should not vary from point to point. Furthermore, it is desirable that the strength of this field should be as high as is practically possible for we have seen that chemical shifts are proportional to field strength. Thus higher field strengths result in increased dispersion of the spectrum. High field strengths also have the advantage of giving rise to stronger absorption signals. The strength of an absorption signal relative to the irreducible background of radiofrequency noise varies with approximately the one and one-half power of the field strength[1] and in the final analysis an increase in field strength can mean a reduction in the total amount of the compound needed for spectral determination, a consideration which is often of considerable importance to the organic chemist.

An electromagnet has the advantage that it is possible to pre-set the field strength at anywhere from zero to its maximum value. This is useful in that the instrument can be adapted for examination of more than one isotope without altering the radiofrequency oscillator. A more important advantage derives from the possibility of measuring the spectrum of the same isotope at different field strengths. This practice sometimes assists the analysis of complex spectra since it differentiates between the field-dependent chemical shifts and the field invariant spin–spin couplings. The principal disadvantage of an electromagnet is that it is difficult to attain the required stability in terms of resolution and field strength without elaborate and expensive equipment. Furthermore, an electromagnet does not usually give a field of high homogeneity without electrical and mechanical manipulation calling for a certain degree of skill on the part of the operator. At present, however, somewhat higher field strengths are attainable with electro-magnets than with permanent magnets.

The operation of instruments which utilize permanent magnets is much simpler. Provided there is adequate thermostating of the equipment, the homogeneous field is always present and few adjustments are necessary. The homogeneity is of the same order as obtainable with electromagnets. No variation of field strength (apart from that necessary for scanning the spectrum) is possible so that there is no means of examining a given isotope at more than one field strength. The stability of permanent magnets in terms of field strength is usually very good; again provided the magnet is efficiently thermostated.

In the preceding chapter we observed that, for liquids, the natural line width of a nuclear resonance signal was governed by the average lifetime of a nucleus in any one spin state. In practice it is frequently, though not always, found that the homogeneity of the static magnetic field is the determining factor. Inhomo-geneity of the magnetic field causes nuclei in different parts of the sample to experi-ence different field strengths and consequently to precess at different frequencies. If the broadening of the signal due to this effect is greater than that governed by spin–spin and spin–lattice relaxation the inhomogeneity of the applied field con-stitutes the limit of resolution.

3.3 THE RADIOFREQUENCY OSCILLATOR

We have seen (p. 8) that in order to induce a nuclear transition it is necessary to provide a rotating electromagnetic field the magnetic component of which moves in a plane perpendicular to the direction of the applied magnetic field. Although the production of such rotating fields is feasible it is more convenient to use a linearly oscillating field. This is possible because such a field may be regarded as being the resultant of two components rotating in phase but in opposite directions as is shown in Fig. 3.1. One of these components will be rotating in the same sense as the precessing nuclear magnet with which it will interact when the frequencies are the same. The other component will have no effect on the nucleus and need not be further considered.

Linearly polarized radiofrequency radiation is precisely that which is generally used in radio communication. Consequently our source of radiant energy is merely a radio transmitter (r.f. oscillator) capable of generating a signal of constant frequency the power of which can be varied if necessary. This signal is fed to a coil situated in the pole gap of the magnet and wound with its axis perpendicular to the direction of the magnetic field. Such an arrangement provides for a magnetic component of the electromagnetic field to rotate in a plane at right angles to the main field direction. Thus, if a sample is placed inside the coil it will be effectively submitted to a rotating magnetic field correctly orientated for the induction of nuclear magnetic transitions.

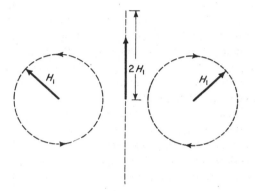

FIG. 3.1 The resolution of a linearly oscillating field into two fields rotating in opposite senses.

3.4 MAGNETIC FIELD SWEEP

The precessing magnetic nuclei can be brought into resonance with the rotating magnetic field by suitable variation of the frequency of either the former or the latter. Alteration of the precessional frequency can be effected by varying the strength of the applied static field while determination of the rotational frequency of the rotating magnetic field, H_1, can be achieved by varying the frequency of the r.f. oscillator. As most commercial instruments employ the practice of varying the applied static field we will describe only this method.

The sweeping or scanning of the static field may be accomplished in two ways. Firstly it is possible to apply a direct current to coils wound on the two pole pieces of the magnet. In the second method a direct current is fed to a pair of Helmholtz coils* which flank the sample with their axis parallel to the direction of the static field. Either method allows the effective value of H_0 to be varied over a small range without detriment to the homogeneity of the field. The first method is only suitable for relatively low sweep rates as high inductance limits the rate of response of H_0 to the superimposed sweep potential. In practice both the methods can be so operated that the rate of change of the sweep field is constant with time; i.e. a linear sweep is employed.

*Each coil has the same number of turns. The separation of the coils is equal to their radius.

3.5 THE DETECTOR

The passage of radiofrequency radiation through the magnetized sample is associated with two phenomena, namely absorption and dispersion. The terms absorption and dispersion have exactly the same meaning here as they have in classical optics and the way in which each depends on the frequency of the radiation is the same in nuclear magnetic resonance as in optics. The line shapes associated with absorption and dispersion are shown in Figs. 3.2 and 3.3. It is clear that the observation of either dispersion or absorption will enable the resonance frequency to be determined. In practice it is usually easier to interpret an absorption spectrum than the corresponding dispersion spectrum.

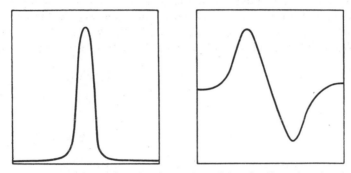

FIG. 3.2   The absorption signal.   FIG. 3.3   The dispersion signal.

Basically the function of the detector is twofold. It must firstly separate the absorption signal from the dispersion signal and secondly it must separate the absorption signal from that supplied by the r.f. oscillator. This second function is necessary because although the amplitude of the applied r.f. signal remains constant it is very much larger than the amplitude of the absorption signal. There are two principal methods of detection. The first involves the measurement of the effect of the absorption and/or dispersion signals at the transmitter coil of the r.f. oscillator.[2] This requires the use of a radiofrequency bridge which functions in very much the same way as the more familiar Wheatstone's bridge. The bridge network balances out the transmitter signal and allows the absorption or dispersion signals to appear as an out-of-balance e.m.f. across the bridge. The out-of-balance signal can be amplified and rectified, and recorded or displayed on an oscilloscope. In order to suppress the unwanted dispersion signal advantage is taken of the fact that the absorption and dispersion signals differ in phase by 90°. If the transmitter signal is not completely balanced out but instead a certain amount of energy *in phase* with the absorption signal is passed by the bridge, the contribution of dispersion to the signal which is fed to the amplifier is negligible. This can be seen from a consideration of Fig. 3.4. OA and OC are vectors representing the absorption and dispersion signals respectively and AB represents the deliberately introduced out-of-balance transmitter signal. Thus the signal which is fed to the amplifier is given by the vector OD. Provided the length of OB is large compared with OC the latter will make a negligible contribution to OD.

The r.f. bridge is so designed that both the phase and amplitude of the out-of-balance transmitter signal can be controlled.

In the above method the one coil which surrounds the sample serves as both a transmitter and a receiver coil. The second method of detection employs a separate

FIG. 3.4   The vector diagram representing the suppression of the dispersion signal by the introduction of leakage in phase with the absorption signal.

receiver coil and is sometimes called the nuclear induction method.[3] If the two coils have their axes at right angles to each other (and also to the direction of the static magnetic field) they will not be coupled. In this way the transmitter signal is separated from the absorption and dispersion signals. Provision is made for a

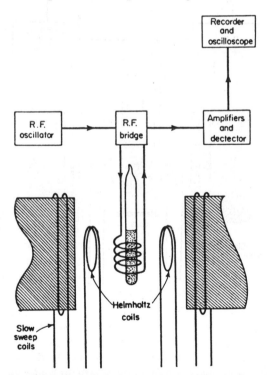

FIG. 3.5   Nuclear magnetic resonance spectrometer. The single coil system.

variable degree of inductive and capacitive coupling between the two coils so that some leakage of the transmitter signal, which is in phase with the absorption signal, can be effected in order to suppress the dispersion signal.

Figures 3.5 and 3.6 are block diagrams illustrating the two methods. A detailed understanding of the origins of the absorption and dispersion signals can be obtained from Bloch's original paper.[4]

3.6 EXPERIMENTAL FACTORS WHICH INFLUENCE NUCLEAR MAGNETIC RESONANCE SPECTRA

There are a number of factors associated with the experimental technique which can alter the shape, strength, and observed frequency of a nuclear magnetic absorption signal. It is important to be aware of these factors and to take them into account before attempting to assign lines in a spectrum.

Homogeneity of the Magnetic Field

We have mentioned that the line width of an absorption signal is frequently determined by the homogeneity of the magnetic field. If a permanent magnet is

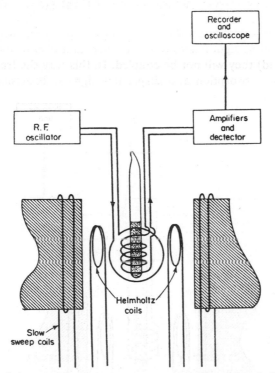

FIG. 3.6   Nuclear magnetic resonance spectrometer. The nuclear induction system.

used the homogeneity will be a more or less constant factor so that the limit of resolution of the instrument will be known. The homogeneity of an electromagnet, on the other hand, can vary considerably from day to day or even over shorter periods. In assessing any spectrum it is necessary to know the resolution at the time of measurement and we therefore require an index of resolution. A convenient estimate of resolving power is provided by the measurement of line width. For this purpose a substance capable of giving a very narrow absorption line should be used. Acetaldehyde is recommended, as the lines of the quartet from the aldehydic proton are extremely sharp.* The line width is expressed as the width (in

*It is important to remove atmospheric oxygen from the sample otherwise the line width may be determined by paramagnetic broadening (p. 12).

cycles per second) of the line measured at half height (see Fig. 3.7). The statement of an index of resolution with published spectra is a desirable practice. Another criterion of resolving power will be introduced later (p. 40).

The homogeneity of the magnetic field between the parallel pole faces of a magnet is greatest in the central region and falls off towards the periphery. For this reason it is desirable that the diameter of the pole pieces should be large (of the order of 10–12 in.) in order to provide an adequate central region which is free from "edge" effects. Clearly, the smaller the volume of homogeneous field required the higher will be the attainable homogeneity. Thus considerations of resolution demand small samples. This requirement has to be balanced against two other variables namely the strength of the absorption signals and the number of nuclei of a given type in the sample under investigation. Thus, in order to obtain observable signals from a compound of low solubility and high molecular weight

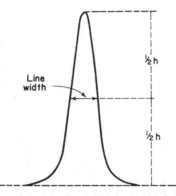

FIG. 3.7 The line width at half height.

it may be necessary to use a large sample of a dilute solution even though such a procedure inevitably results in decreased resolution. In other words, we have generally to compromise between the conflicting requirements of resolving power and signal strength.

The effect of the finite volume of the sample on the attainable resolution can be reduced to some extent by spinning the sample tube about the y-axis (Fig. 3.8). If the tube is spun fast enough (p. 38) nuclei lying on a given circle in or parallel to the xz plane will experience a field which is the average of the fields at each and every point on that circle so that the apparent homogeneity is increased.

The homogeneity in the y direction is of course unaffected by sample spinning. With electromagnets the homogeneity in this direction can be improved by a technique called "cycling". When an electromagnet is switched on and left for a period to attain an equilibrium state it is frequently found that the central region of the pole pieces have become more intensely magnetized than their periphery so that the field has the dome shaped contour depicted in Fig. 3.9A. Good homogeneity is confined to a small area corresponding to the top of the dome. If the current in the coils of the magnet is now raised above its operating value for a short time (1–5 min) and then returned to its original value the magnetization of the peripheral region is increased so that the dome contour is flattened and the

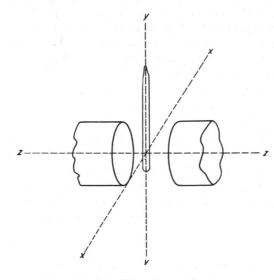

FIG. 3.8 Definition of co-ordinate axes.

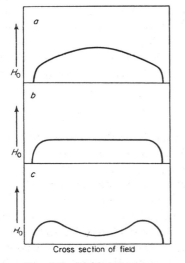

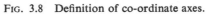
Cross section of field

FIG. 3.9 Field contours.

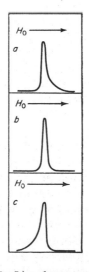

FIG. 3.10 Line shapes associated with different field contours.

region of good homogeneity enlarged. The term "cycling" refers to the procedure of successively raising the current to higher and higher values until a comparatively flat contour (Fig. 3.9B) is obtained. Raising the current to too high a value results in a "dished" contour (Fig. 3.9C) corresponding to three small regions of good homogeneity. The character of the field contour can affect the shape of absorption signals. Coupling between the r.f. field and the cylindrical sample is greatest at the axis of the sample. Therefore, if the sample is situated at the top of a "dome" and the field swept from low to high fields through resonance, the centre of the sample being at a slightly higher field comes into resonance first, and as this part of the sample is strongly coupled it gives rise to a strong signal. As the sweep continues the outer parts of the sample now resonate but as they are less strongly coupled the strength of the signal tails off. The resulting line shape is shown in Fig. 3.10A. By a similar argument it follows that a sample situated at the bottom of a "dish" will have the line shape depicted in Fig. 3.10C. Ideally, the field contour should be flat so that symmetrical signals (Fig. 3.10B) can be observed.

Sample Spinning

The practice of spinning samples to increase resolution was considered on p. 36. For this procedure to be effective it is necessary that the rotational frequency should be in excess of the desired resolution expressed in cycles per second. Thus two or three revolutions per second is adequate if we wish to achieve a resolving power of $0 \cdot 5$ c/s. If the spinning frequency is too low the averaging of the field is incomplete and the main absorption signal is accompanied by side bands as illustrated in Fig. 3.11. In practice, side bands can also result from uneven spinning of the sample tube so that care must be taken to use tubes which spin smoothly. The spacing of side bands is symmetric about the main band and is equal to the spinning frequency or some multiple thereof. Spinning side bands can therefore be identified by comparison of spectra obtained using different spinning frequencies. Very high spinning frequencies can cause the formation of a vortex which may extend into the operative region of the sample. This is to be avoided since it can cause a serious reduction in resolution.

Sweep Rate

The rate at which the magnetic field is varied for the purpose of scanning a spectrum can have a profound effect on the shape of absorption signals. Figure 3.12 shows the proton signal from water measured with an extremely high sweep rate and it is seen that rapid sweeping is associated with considerable distortion of the signal. The distortion is described as a "wiggle" or "ringing" and it occurs after the magnetic field has passed through the resonance value. The wiggle depicted in Fig. 3.12 decays exponentially with time. The origin of the effect can be described in the following way. The Boltzmann excess of nuclei in the ground state corresponds to a magnetization of the sample in the direction parallel to the applied field. At resonance, part of this magnetization appears as a rotating component of magnetization in the plane perpendicular to the applied field. It is in fact this rotating component of magnetization which induces the absorption and dispersion signals in the receiver coil. If at resonance the r.f. field, H_1, is suddenly removed the rotating component of magnetization will not immediately vanish but rather it

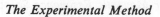

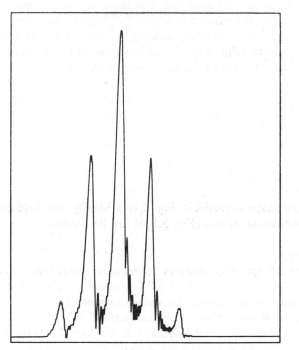

FIG. 3.11 The proton signal of water with spinning side bands caused by the use of **too** low a spinning frequency.

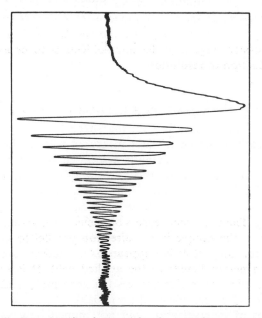

FIG. 3.12 The distortion of a signal caused by the use of a very high sweep rate.

will decay exponentially at a rate determined by the relaxation times of the nuclei giving rise to the signal. A similar situation results from rapid sweeping through the resonance condition. In this circumstance, however, the frequency of the rotating component of magnetization varies with the changing sweep field, and as a result the induced signals are alternately in and out of phase with the applied r.f. field, the frequency of which is constant. The result is the characteristic beating pattern illustrated in Fig. 3.12. Evidently the shorter the relaxation times T_1 and T_2 the less will be the distortion due to ringing. Since T_2 includes the field inhomogeneity (p. 35), the observation of ringing is a good indication of a homogeneous field.

The obvious way of removing the unwanted ringing from recorded signals is to use a slow sweep. There are, however, several factors which place a lower limit on permissible sweep rates. If, as is invariably the case, we ultimately wish to determine the relative separations of bands in a spectrum it is vital that the sweep rate should not vary throughout the recording of the spectrum. However, the static magnetic field is usually subject to small long term non-linear variations which are superimposed upon the sweep and consequently can introduce serious errors if the sweep rate is too low. Saturation (p. 13) can also limit the permissible sweep rate. Saturation, it will be remembered, amounts to the equalization of the population of spin states and the consequent destruction of the absorption condition. If the sweep field were held at the resonance value saturation would be observed as a progressive decrease in the amplitude of the absorption signal. Very slow sweep rates approximate to this situation so that if the saturation factor, Z_0 (p. 13), is small, loss of signal strength and distortion (see below) will result.

Signal-to-Noise Ratio

The signal appearing at the receiver coil is extremely weak and requires considerable amplification prior to rectification and recording. The limit to which the signal can be amplified is determined by the ratio of its amplitude to the mean amplitude of the background radiofrequency noise. We may assume that commercial instruments have been designed to reduce the intrinsic noise factor of the instrument to a minimum so that we may confine our attention to some general considerations over which the operator has some measure of control.

To maintain the noise at a minimum, care should be taken with the selection of sample tubes. Sample tubes which spin unevenly can very often increase the noise level. A proportion of the background noise appears after rectification as very short term fluctuations and can be eliminated by using a relatively long time constant (*ca.* 1·0 sec) prior to the recording or display stage. Provision for the adjustment of the frequency response is usually incorporated in commercial instruments. When long time constants are used it is important that the sweep rate should be slow enough to permit a faithful response to the actual absorption signals.

The most effective way of maintaining a satisfactory signal-to-noise ratio is to provide for a sufficient number of the magnetic nuclei in the operative region of the sample; that is, the region of the sample which is effectively coupled with the r.f. system. We have already seen that high resolution requires that the volume of this region should be small and we can therefore envisage two important factors, namely solubility and molecular weight, which may limit the number of magnetic nuclei which can be contained in this space. We have already noted that our measurements must be confined to the liquid state so that solid compounds have to be examined as solutions. We will see presently that the choice of really suitable solvents is very limited and we will frequently find that signal strength is determined by considerations of solubility. It is sometimes of advantage to use heated sample holders but the introduction of the extra equipment into the pole gap inevitably results in decreased resolution. A sample consisting of 0·2 ml of a 0·15 *M* solution usually gives a satisfactory proton spectrum. This is a very approximate value and the actual requirements vary considerably from case to case. For instance, Shoolery and Rogers[4] have recorded the proton spectrum (at 40 Mc) from only 1·35 mg of a steroid.

R.F. Power Level

In theory of course, the signal strength can be increased by raising the power of the r.f. field. However, this cannot be continued indefinitely as ultimately saturation (p. 13) of the absorption signals will occur. It seems likely that the power limit created by saturation could often be raised by introducing low concentrations of a paramagnetic substance, such as diphenylpicrylhydrazyl, which will decrease the spin–lattice relaxation time and hence increase the saturation factor Z_0. Some preliminary experiments by the author indicate that such a procedure does not significantly effect proton chemical shifts provided the concentration of the radical is low. There will of course be an optimum radical concentration for each system since the use of too high a concentration results in paramagnetic broadening.

Apart from causing a decrease in signal strength, appreciable r.f. saturation will result in distortion of absorption signals since, of the nuclei constituting the Boltzmann excess in the lower state, those with precisely the correct precessional frequency will be most readily lost on irradiation so that saturation affects the centre of the absorption signal more than the outer parts. Saturation therefore causes an apparent broadening of the resonance line.

3.7 CALIBRATION OF SPECTRA AND THE DETERMINATION OF SHIELDING VALUES

Of all the stages in the measurement of a nuclear magnetic resonance spectrum the determination of relative line positions and the subsequent derivation of shielding values for nuclei in various environments is without doubt the most important to the organic chemist. It is therefore of paramount importance that the principles involved should be thoroughly understood.

The organic chemist is familiar with infrared and ultraviolet spectroscopic methods in which the absolute line positions are obtained directly from the instrument. For a number of reasons this practice is not possible with nuclear resonance spectroscopy. Indeed the determination of absolute frequencies to $\pm 1·0$ c/s would require measurements to be made with an accuracy of 1 part in 10^8. Fortunately relative line positions can be readily determined with an accuracy of $\pm 1·0$ c/s and in certain circumstances with even higher precision. Our approach must therefore be based on relative line positions and we shall need to decide on a standard line position for each isotope.

There are three principal methods of measuring line separations in a nuclear magnetic resonance spectrum. Of these the most widely used is the "side band" technique. Let us suppose we are examining the spectrum of water. Under normal conditions we obtain only one line. If we now apply, say, a 100 c/s sinusoidal e.m.f. from an audiofrequency oscillator to either the sweep coils or to the r.f. transmitter we observe that the original proton line of water is now symmetrically flanked by pairs of lines as illustrated in Fig. 3.13. It can be shown[5] that the separation of the first pair of side bands from the main signal corresponds to the frequency of the

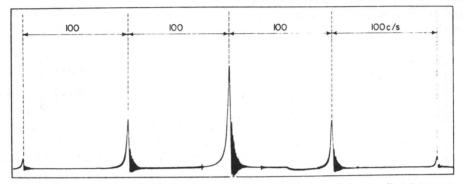

FIG. 3.13   The pattern of side bands produced by modulation of the supplied field with a sinusoidal e.m.f. (100 c/s.).

sinusoidal e.m.f., in this instance 100 c/s. The separations of the subsequent side bands are multiples of 100 c/s. In this way we are able to calibrate the chart paper for the particular sweep rate and chart speed employed. If we apply this technique to a many-line spectrum then, provided we can identify the side bands, we can again calibrate the chart and so determine the separations, in cycles per second, of the various lines in the spectrum. Commercial audiofrequency oscillators are suitable for production of side bands by modulation. The frequency of the modulation will usually be within one cycle of the value set on the dial and this accuracy is adequate for most of our purposes. The most serious source of error in the calibration made by this method arises from the non-linearity of the magnetic sweep caused by the superimposition of long term fluctuations in the main magnetic field (p. 40). Such errors can be eliminated in the following way. We measure the separation of two lines in a spectrum by varying the modulation frequency until the first side band of one signal is coincident with the second signal. The frequency separation can then be read off directly from the dial of the oscillator and the value thus obtained is now independent of the linearity of the sweep. The superimposition method is however difficult and tedious to apply to a complicated spectrum and an interpolation method is usually adopted. When using the interpolation method it is important to check for variations in the sweep rate. This can be done by comparing the results obtained for several determinations of the spectrum. Alternatively a number of side bands can be introduced at regular intervals in the spectrum (Fig. 3.14). The linearity of the sweep may then be established by showing that the distances between successive side bands are in the same ratio as their corresponding frequency separations. Even when this method is employed it is wise to calibrate a second spectrum, in which the field is swept in the opposite direction, and check the consistency of the results.

A substance possessing well-defined absorption bands, the separations of which are known, can be used to calibrate the spectrum of another compound. If a sealed capillary containing the former is added to the sample of the latter the two spectra can be determined simultaneously. Provided the signals of the standard compound are recognizable, a calibration of the combined spectrum can be made. Toluene, which gives just two absorption lines separated by 197 c/s at 40 Mc has been used for calibrating proton spectra. Because of the inflexibility of this method and because it involves large interpolations it is not recommended for accurate work.

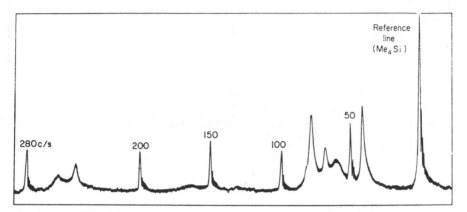

FIG. 3.14 Calibration of a spectrum by the side-band technique. The spectrum of β-Carotene in $CDCl_3$. The side bands have been generated by modulation of the signal of a reference substance, tetramethylsilane. Any strong, sharp signal in a spectrum can be used in this way.

The third method of determining line separations, known as the "wiggle beat" technique is ideal for measuring small separations (< 15 c/s) such as observed for many spin multiplets. We have seen that rapid sweeping through sharp signals produces a distortion known as ringing (p. 38). The ringing pattern from a single absorption peak decays exponentially. If two closely situated signals are rapidly traversed the decay pattern of the first interferes with that of the second. The result is a decay envelope exhibiting a series of maxima and minima (Fig. 3.15). The number of maxima observed per second is equal to the separation (in cycles per second) of the two signals and can be determined by displaying the pattern on an oscilloscope with a known time base. Alternatively the pattern can be recorded on a rapidly moving chart, together with time intervals of one second marked off with a fiducial marker. The recorder used for this purpose must have a very rapid response. In suitable cases an accuracy of ± 0.1 c/s can be obtained.

If we are to compare the positions of absorption lines of one compound with those of other compounds it is necessary to refer all line positions to some standard position. The choice of the standard line position is arbitrary but we must be able to identify it in every spectrum. At first sight we might suppose that this could always be accomplished by adding to a sample a sealed capillary containing a standard substance giving a single sharp absorption signal which we could then use as a standard line position. When used in this way the standard is called **an external reference**. However, this technique is only legitimate if the effective fields experienced by the sample and reference are the same or if the difference between them is constant for all samples. Now the field experienced by a molecule in a sample will depend on the shape and magnetic susceptibility of the sample. This is expressed in equation (1):

$$H_{\text{effective}} = H^0[1-(N_s-N_m)K] \tag{1}$$

where K is the volume susceptibility of the sample and N_s and N_m are shape factors for the sample and the hypothetical cavity containing the molecule, respectively. If

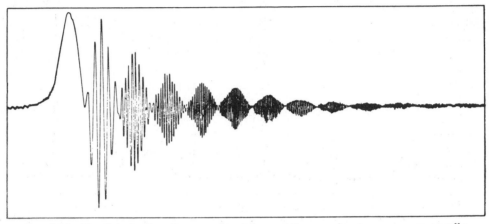

FIG. 3.15 The "ringing" pattern produced by rapidly sweeping two or more equally spaced signals.

the molecular cavity is assumed to be spherical, the term (N_s-N_m) reduces to $2\pi/3 = 2 \cdot 09$ for a cylindrical sample orientated with its axis perpendicular to the field (i.e. the normal experimental position of the sample). A similar expression holds for the capillary reference. Bothner-By and Glick[6] have shown that the line position of an external reference is independent of the susceptibility of the sample. Therefore, the field experienced by the sample is not equal to that experienced by the external reference. Furthermore, since K will vary from sample to sample the difference between H_{eff} for sample and reference will not be constant. For these reasons *the values of line positions obtained by the external reference technique will depend on the volume susceptibility of the sample and will not be a true measure of intramolecular shielding.*

In principle it should be possible to correct for the susceptibility contribution either by determining K or by using spherical samples ($N_s = N_r$). However, Bothner-By and Glick[6] have shown empirically that the correction, $(N_s-N_r)K$, does not depend solely on the shape factors and that (N_s-N_r) may have values between $2 \cdot 3 - 3 \cdot 0$ instead of the theoretical $2 \cdot 09$. Insertion of numerical values into equation (3·1) reveals that the uncertainty of the correction could result in errors of an order of magnitude greater than we can tolerate.

The use of an external reference can be adapted so as to give reliable shielding values. To do this it is necessary to measure the line positions relative to the external reference from spectra of the compound in solutions of varying concentration, and to extrapolate to infinite dilution. Extrapolation to infinite dilution is, in effect, an extrapolation to the volume susceptibility of the solvent. Therefore, if the spectra of all compounds are determined in the same solvent and the line positions extrapolated to infinite dilution in each case, the results obtained will permit a direct comparison of the relative intramolecular shielding of nuclei*. The obvious disadvantages of this procedure are that a number of measurements at different concentrations is required for each compound and that the same solvent must be used throughout.

When using the external reference technique care should be taken with the selection of the capillary containing the reference substance. The capillary should be accurately cylindrical and should not cause the sample to spin unevenly. The use of precision coaxial sample tubes has been recommended.[7]

The difficulties of obtaining a constant susceptibility difference between reference and sample are best avoided by using an internal reference. An internal reference is actually dissolved in the sample. The reference substance therefore experiences exactly the same field as the compound under investigation and the question of volume susceptibilities does not arise. Thus, although the absolute line position of the reference varies with the susceptibility of the sample-reference mixture the relative positions of the sample and reference signals remain constant. There is, however, an inherent danger in this method of standardization which derives from the assumption that admixture of the reference compound with the sample does not alter the absolute line position of the former other than by virtue of the change in volume susceptibility. If there is any chemical interaction, however weak, between the reference and solvent or sample molecules, the above assumption is no longer necessarily valid. The data in Table 3.1 give some indication of the

TABLE 3.1   A COMPARISON OF INTERNAL REFERENCE COMPOUNDS

Reference	Line position of the aromatic protons of ethylbenzene (c/s from tetramethylsilane)
Chloroform	325·5
Methylenedichloride	317·5
Dioxane	290·5
Cyclohexane	281·5
Tetramethylsilane	282·0
Tetramethylsilane*	284·5
External reference†	284·4

*added to a 10 per cent solution of ethylbenzene in CCl_4.
†by extrapolation to infinite dilution in CCl_4.

inconsistencies which may result from an injudicious choice of the internal reference. The data in Table 3.1 have been compiled in the following way: the positions of the absorption lines of the reference compounds relative to the single line of

* Water should never be used as an external reference because its line position varies with temperature.

tetramethylsilane were determined with an external reference by extrapolation to infinite dilution in carbon tetrachloride; small quantities of each reference were added to samples of pure ethylbenzene and the separation between the reference lines and the aromatic proton line of ethylbenzene were measured; these separations were then referred to the tetramethylsilane line which was given the arbitrary value of zero. The results should be compared with the last entry in the table which is the relative line position of the aromatic proton of ethylbenzene, obtained with an external reference by extrapolation to infinite dilution in carbon tetrachloride. It is evident that compounds such as chloroform, methylene dichloride and dioxane are unsuitable for use as internal references, presumably because they are specifically solvated by the sample.[7]

We can now outline the properties which are demanded of a satisfactory internal reference.

(a) It must be chemically inert to a high degree.
(b) It must be magnetically isotropic, or nearly so.
(c) It should give a single, sharp, and readily recognizable absorption signal.
(d) It should be readily miscible with a wide variety of solvents and other organic liquids.
(e) It should be relatively volatile in order to facilitate the recovery of valuable sample material.

The most suitable reference compound at present available for proton spectroscopy is tetramethylsilane, $[(CH_3)_4Si]$. Its use as an internal standard was first proposed by Tiers[8] and there is little doubt that it will be widely used for this purpose. Tetramethylsilane is chemically very inert and, as the twelve protons are spherically distributed, it is magnetically isotropic. In addition it is volatile (b.p. 27°) and miscible with organic solvents. It gives a single absorption line. Tiers has shown that the use of tetramethylsilane as an internal reference corresponds closely to the method employing an external reference at infinite dilution. The data in Table 3.2 demonstrates the equivalence of the two methods. Cyclohexane is another suitable internal reference. Of the two compounds tetramethylsilane is to be preferred as its absorption line occupies a unique position in the spectrum being at higher frequency than all the common types of organic protons.

In order to obtain the most reliable shielding values with an internal reference it is important to *make the measurements on a dilute solution* (< 15 per cent w/v) *of a compound in a suitable solvent* (see below). The actual concentration employed is usually determined by the signal-to-noise ratio. For the greatest precision it is recommended that two internal standards, tetramethylsilane and cyclohexane, should be used. This procedure is particularly valuable if unsuitable solvents have to be used. The constancy of the separation of the two reference lines is then a partial check on the invariance of both.

Finally, we must decide on the most convenient way of expressing shielding values. We have seen (p. 19) that the chemical shift is proportional to field strength or to what is equivalent, the r.f. oscillator frequency. It is thus desirable to express line positions in a form which is independent of the field strength and frequency. This can be done by using the chemical shift parameter δ defined by equation (2)

$$\delta = (H_s - H_r)/H_r \tag{2}$$

where H_s and H_r are the field strengths corresponding to resonance for a particular nucleus in the sample and the reference, respectively. As we usually calibrate our spectra in cycles per second we may rewrite equation (2) as (3) where Δ, the line

$$\delta = \frac{\Delta \cdot 10^6}{\text{Oscillator frequency (c/s)}} \quad (3)$$

separation between sample and reference, is negative if the sample line is at a

TABLE 3.2—THE EQUIVALENCE OF LINE POSITIONS OBTAINED USING TETRAMETHYLSILANE AS AN INTERNAL REFERENCE WITH THOSE OBTAINED EMPLOYING AN EXTERNAL REFERENCE AND EXTRAPOLATION, TO INFINITE DILUTION IN CARBON TETRACHLORIDE

The line positions are given as values of τ defined below

Compound*	Internal†	External‡
C_6H_6	2·73	2·74
$C_6H_5C_2H_5$	2·89	2·89
$(C_6H_5CH_2)_2$	2·89	2·89
p-$C_6H_4(CH_3)_2$	3·05	3·05
Cyclooctatetraene	4·31	4·26
CH_3NO_2	5·72	5·69
$C_6H_5OCH_3$	6·27	6·31
CH_3OH	6·62	6·60
$(C_6H_5CH_2)_2$	7·13	7·13
$C_6H_5CH_2CH_3$	7·38	7·42
$C_6H_5CH_3$	7·66	7·67
$(CH_3CO)_2O$	7·81	7·81
CH_2I	7·84	7·81
CH_3COCH_3	7·915	7·91
CH_3CO_2H	7·93	7·90
CH_3CN	8·03	8·10
Cyclohexane	8·56	8·51

* The protons to which the values refer are printed in bold-face type.
† All measurements were made on dilute (1–6% v/v) solutions in CCl_4.
‡ These values were obtained from various sources (see Ref. 8 for references).

lower frequency than the reference line. The factor 10^6 is included to give convenient numbers (for proton spectroscopy) so that δ, which is dimensionless, is thus expressed in parts per million (p.p.m.). If the signal of tetramethylsilane is taken as the standard proton line position δ will be negative for common organic protons. To obviate the inconvenience of using negative values Tiers has introduced the quantity $\tau = 10 - \delta$, which is positive for all but very acidic protons if the standard line position is that of tetramethylsilane. As we shall use τ exclusively in the remainder of this book the full expression is given in equation (4).

$$\tau(\text{p.p.m.}) = 10 - \frac{\Delta(\text{Me}_4\text{Si}) \cdot 10^6}{\text{Oscillator frequence (c/s)}} \quad (4)$$

We note that the larger the value of τ, the greater is the magnetic shielding of the nucleus to which it refers. An important point to remember is that the spin–spin coupling constant, J, is independent of the applied field and should therefore be expressed in cycles per second rather than in units of τ.

Tiers[9] has also developed a standard procedure for measuring and expressing the shielding values in fluorine resonance spectroscopy. He advocates the use of CCl_3F both as a solvent and reference and has introduced the quantity ϕ, defined as $10^6 (H_s - H_{CCl_3F})/H_{CCl_3F}$, as the fluorine chemical shift parameter which is determined by extrapolation to infinite dilution.

3.8 SOLVENTS

The choice of suitable solvents for proton spectroscopy of organic compounds is very limited. As well as being capable of giving fairly concentrated solutions (5–20 per cent) of organic compounds a satisfactory solvent should be chemically inert, magnetically isotropic and preferably devoid of hydrogen atoms. Carbon tetrachloride is the ideal solvent and should be used whenever possible. However, many compounds are insufficiently soluble in carbon tetrachloride and other solvents have to be used. Carbon disulphide, chloroform and deuterochloroform are often suitable and the τ-values measured in these solvents correspond closely to measurements in carbon tetrachloride. Other solvents such as benzene, pyridine, dioxane, acetone, dimethylformamide, and acetonitrile, have to be used in certain cases and it is probable that the τ-values so obtained may require corrections of the order of 0·1 p.p.m. Measurements made on pure liquids are also subject to error particularly if the compounds are aromatic (see Table 3.1; fifth and sixth entries) and it is for this reason that measurements on dilute solutions are preferred.

3.9 MEASUREMENT OF INTENSITIES

The intensity of an absorption signal in a spectrum is proportional to the number of nuclei which give rise to the signal (p. 20) and for this reason the determination of relative intensities can be of considerable value in structural organic chemistry. The intensity of an absorption signal is given by the area which it encloses. The determination of the relative areas, and hence relative intensities, of signals in a spectrum will only be meaningful if certain precautions are taken.

Since, within any spectrum, line shapes may vary considerably, line heights are seldom proportional to areas. In the case of a spectrum in which the individual lines are well separated it is often possible to reduce each line to approximately the same shape by using a sufficiently inhomogeneous field. If the signals are now recorded at high sweep rates, their relative heights become a good measure of relative intensities. However, the examination of most complex molecules requires the use of maximum resolution so that relative intensities can only be obtained from direct area measurements. If a wide chart paper is used area measurements can be conveniently made with a planimeter. An alternative, which is also useful for narrow charts, involves the cutting out and weighing of each band. Whichever method is employed a number of determinations on several recordings should be made and an average value computed. The observed areas are very sensitive to a number of experimental factors. Any variation in sweep rate during the recording of the spectrum introduces serious errors. Excessive background noise lowers the accuracy of area measurements by introducing uncertainties in the location of the base line. It is also important to suppress the dispersion signal by carefully adjusting the in-phase leakage (p. 33) and to reduce distortion due to ringing to a minimum as described above (p. 40). Solvent blanks should be run under the same conditions to insure that they do not absorb in the region under examination. It is important to be sure that the recorder used is linear.

The relative strengths of signals are only proportional to the numbers of nuclei in each group in a molecule if the saturation factors, Z_0, of each signal are negligible. For this reason area ratios should be determined at several r.f. powers (i.e. several values of H_1) and extrapolated to zero power. It is usually sufficient to determine the relative areas for two rather different powers and show that there is no significant variation.

An excellent treatment of the factors which enter into intensity measurements has been given by Williams.[10] He particularly draws attention to the error which is incurred if the amount of leakage introduced to suppress the dispersion signal is too low, and he has plotted this error as a function of the ratio of the maximum signal voltage to the leakage voltage.

It is possible to arrange for the simultaneous recording and electronic integration of signals but as yet this refinement is not a feature of commercial instruments.

REFERENCES

1. E. R. ANDREW, *Nuclear Magnetic Resonance*, Cambridge University Press, 1955, p. 66.
2. N. BLOEMERGEN, E. M. PURCELL and R. V. POUND, *Phys. Rev.* **73**, 679 (1948).
3. F. BLOCH, W. W. HANSEN and M. PACKARD, *ibid.* **70**, 474 (1946).
4. F. BLOCH, *ibid*, 460.
5. W. A. ANDERSON, *ibid.* **102**, 151 (1056).
6. A. A. BOTHNER-BY and R. E. GLICK, *J. Chem. Phys.* **26**, 1647 (1957).
7. J. R. ZIMMERMAN and M. R. FOSTER, *J. Phys. Chem.* **61**, 282 (1957).
8. G. V. D. TIERS, *ibid.* **62**, 1151 (1958).
9. G. FILIPOVICH and G. V. D. TIERS, *ibid.* **63**, 761 (1959).
10. R. B. WILLIAMS, *Ann. New York Acad. Sci.* **70**, 890 (1958).

CHAPTER 4

THE CORRELATION OF THE CHEMICAL SHIFT WITH MOLECULAR STRUCTURE. HYDROGEN BONDED TO CARBON

4.1 INTRODUCTION

IN THE previous chapter we saw that it is possible to measure proton resonance line positions relative to an internal standard with an accuracy of about ± 0.025 p.p.m. The value of such data will depend on two principal considerations. In the first place it is necessary to assign the lines or multiplets in a spectrum of a molecule to specific atoms or groups of equivalent atoms in the molecule. For the purpose of the present and the following chapter we will assume that this is possible and reserve our discussion of the analyses of spectra until Chapter 6. This, of course, is not the sequence in which the subject has been developed but is more closely related to the approach of the organic chemist. In other words, now that there is a body of empirical data to draw on we use chemical shift correlations to assist in making spectral assignments.

The second consideration concerns the assumed invariance of the line position of the internal reference. The validity of this assumption is, in effect, subject to an experimental test every time we examine a spectrum, and the method using an internal reference will stand or fall according to the outcome of these tests. Thus if the internal reference is performing its proper function we will expect that the τ-value for, say, an aliphatic methoxyl group will be reasonably constant for a wide variety of molecules in which it is present. Inevitably examples will be found in which the τ-value of the methoxyl group deviates appreciably from the expected value. We have then to decide whether this is the fault of the internal standard or whether in fact an anomolous shielding mechanism is operating. Investigators who have had experience with internal standards such as tetramethylsilane and cyclohexane have found grounds for considerable confidence in the invariance of their line positions and it seems most unlikely that deviations greater than 0.15 p.p.m. can occur even when unfavourable solvents are used. We may therefore with some confidence proceed to attempt a correlation between τ-values and molecular structure.

The first major compilation of chemical shift data was made by Meyer, Saika, and Gutowsky[1] in 1953. The accuracy of line position measurements attainable at this time was only ± 0.3 p.p.m., but in spite of this uncertainty, which is of an order higher than present day requirements, the results obtained indicated for the first time the tremendous potential value of nuclear magnetic resonance spectroscopy to the organic chemist. Recently, two other sources of data have been compiled. The first of these is due to Chamberlain and his co-workers[2] of the Humble Oil and Refining Company. They point out that their data, which were obtained at 30 Mc on a prototype instrument, leave much to be desired both with regard to resolution and standardization. Nevertheless, their catalogue remains a particularly valuable source of data. The second compilation is that of G. Van Dyke Tiers of the Minnesota Mining and Manufacturing Company and includes some 700 τ-values obtained with an accuracy of ± 0.025 p.p.m. by internal standardization against tetramethylsilane. These two catalogues form the basis for correlating proton chemical shifts with molecular structure.

In this chapter we will consider only hydrogen nuclei which are directly bound to carbon and we will derive much of our information from a consideration of acyclic systems. Here it must be emphasized very strongly that, *τ-values derived from acyclic systems do not necessarily correlate well with those derived from cyclic systems.* The reason for this can be readily understood if we realize that in an acyclic molecule a nucleus, such as a proton α to a hydroxyl group, experiences a shielding which is the weighted average of all possible conformations of the molecule. If the same grouping (—CH(OH)—) is part of a cyclic system it may well be confined to just one conformation and hence experience a shielding which is significantly different from the acyclic analogue. For the same reason we do not expect that the τ-value of a ring proton in a flexible cyclohexane system to be the same as a structurally similar proton in a rigidly fused ring system. These considerations will receive closer attention in Chapter 7 where we specifically consider stereochemical problems.

Each of the following sections dealing with aliphatic protons are designated by an appropriate structure involving a methyl group and it is to be understood that the analogous methylene and methine types will be discussed under the same heading. Thus the section headed CH_3—X also deals with —CH_2—X and $>$CH—X. All values are in units of τ and it may be assumed, unless otherwise stated, that they have been obtained by use of an internal reference under the most favourable conditions. The characteristic τ-values or shifts which appear in the various tables are often averages of observations on a number of compounds. Certain conventions have been adopted. Firstly, values obtained from measurements on only one compound are printed in italics. Secondly, the observed spread in the τ-values for a given type of proton in a number of different molecules will be stated explicitly only if it exceeds ± 0.10 p.p.m. Thirdly, when τ-values are appended to structural formulae the protons to which they refer will be printed in bold face type. Finally, we shall use the adjectives *paramagnetic* and *diamagnetic* to denote shifts to lower and higher frequencies (and fields), respectively.

4.2 ALIPHATIC PROTONS

A. CH_3—C$\lessgtr$

In the absence of deshielding effects induced by neighbouring atoms or groups, the protons of methyl groups are usually the most highly shielded of all the common organic types. For this reason and because they usually give strong (3-proton) signals they are often readily recognizable features of a proton spectrum. The expected position of the methyl group in a saturated hydrocarbon lies between 9.05 and 9.15 (Table 4.1). In certain rigid cyclic systems methyl protons can absorb at slightly higher frequencies (up to 9.40). One of the methyl group in 2-phenylbutane is also found at 9.20. The explanation in this case is doubtless the same as postulated for the anomolous position of some methylene groups in *p*-polymethylenebenzenes (p. 18). Evidently there is considerable population of those conformations in which the 4-methyl group lies over the plane of the benzene ring and in the diamagnetic part of the field associated with the ring current.

TABLE 4.1 METHYL GROUPS IN SATURATED
HYDROCARBONS

Hydrocarbon	τ
$CH_3.CH_3$	9·12
$CH_3.CH_2.CH_3$	9·10
$CH_3.CH_2.CH_2.CH_3$	9·10
$CH_3.(CH_2)_{16}.CO_2CH_3$	9·12
$(CH_3)_3.CH$	9·11
$(CH_3)_4.C$	9·06
Methylcyclohexane	9·08

Acyclic methylene groups are appreciably less shielded than methyl groups and there appears to be a further small reduction on passing to the methine type although it is difficult to find examples of the latter in which the true chemical shift of the methine proton can be accurately determined (cf. p. 89). The shielding of protons in the alicyclic series is somewhat dependent on ring size. This effect is most pronounced in cyclopropane in which the protons are more heavily shielded than methyl groups. The simple polymethylenes exhibit single sharp lines indicating a rapid conformational interchange (p. 28). Methylcyclohexane on the other hand exhibits a broad band near 8·5. There is little doubt that the interchange of conformation is also rapid in this compound but the possible conformations are no longer equivalent so that there is a tendency for the methylene hydrogen atoms to lose their equivalence and divide into axial and equatorial types. Once this happens extensive spin–spin coupling occurs and only a broad unresolved band is observed. A similar situation exists in rigidly fused systems such as encountered in the steroids and higher terpenes. The methylene groups in these molecules produce a broad hump between 7·5 and 9·0 in which the only recognizable features arise from methyl groups.[4] Some values of methylene and methine absorption in saturated systems are given in Table 4.2.

TABLE 4.2 METHYLENE AND METHINE GROUPS IN
SATURATED HYDROCARBONS

Hydrocarbon	τ
$CH_3.(CH_2)_n.CH_3$	8·75
Cyclopropane	9·78
Cyclopentane	8·49
Cyclohexane	8·56
Cycloheptane	8·47
$(CH_3)_3CH$	∼8·5

Substituents of the type —CH_2X (i.e. the system CH_3—C$\leq$$CH_2X$), where X is Cl, Br, I, OH, OR, CO, N$<$, etc., usually cause slight de-shielding of the methyl group which now falls in the region 8·90–9·10. Presumably, methylene and methine protons in analogous situations are similarly affected but in practice molecules of this type will often give rise to broad band envelopes so that the assignment of a frequency to any one methylene or methine hydrogen atom will not be feasible.

Substituents attached to the same carbon atom as a methyl group (i.e. CH_3—C$\leq$X) cause somewhat larger shifts which can be very useful in structure determination. In all cases the shifts are to lower frequencies (see Table 4.3).

TABLE 4.3 THE DESHIELDING OF ALKYL PROTONS BY β-SUBSTITUENTS

Nature of X	Shifts (p.p.m.) to lower frequencies		
	CH_3—C—X	CH_2—C—X	CH—C—X
—C$<$ Y*	0·0–0·15	0·0–0·15	0·0–0·15
F		0·17	
Cl	0·62	0·58–0·32	0·02
Br	0·81	0·63–0·30	0·24
I	1·00	0·56–0·33	0·43
OH, OAlkyl	0·275	0·10	
OAcyl	0·37		
—CH—CH₂ (O)	0·40		
NH₂, NHAlkyl, N(Alkyl)₂	0·10	0·05	
SH, SAlkyl	0·45	0·31	
NO₂	0·67		
C = C	0·10	0·05	
C ≡ C		0·05	
—CHO, COAlkyl	0·18		
CO₂H, CO₂Alkyl	0·25		
C ≡ N		0·42	
Ph	0·35	0·35	

* Y is any common functional group e.g. Cl, Br, I, OH, OR, CO, N$<$ etc.

Thus, —OH and —O.COR substituents reduce the methyl frequency by *ca.* 0·30 p.p.m. For an —SH substituent the shift is somewhat larger (0·45) while the halogens induce shifts of 0·6, 0·8, and 1·0 respectively. Evidently the shielding by a group β to an alkyl proton is largely controlled by its diamagnetic anisotropy with a smaller contribution from its inductive effect. For simple atomic substituents the shift to lower fields increases from left to right across the periodic table (—I effect) and also down the table (diamagnetic polarizability). β-Phenyl substituents exert a paramagnetic effect indicating that the alkyl group spends an appreciable fraction of its time in or near the plane of the aromatic nucleus. The shifts indicated in Table 4.3 also appear to apply roughly to simple cyclohexane derivatives but significant variations are found in rigid ring systems. An example of the uncertainties which exist in rigid systems is provided by a comparison of the resonance frequencies of the protons at C_{18} in the epimeric 11α- and 11β-hydroxy-Δ^4-pregnene-3:10-diones. The 11α-hydroxyl group has a negligible effect whereas in the β-isomer the hydroxyl group induces a paramagnetic shift of 0·20 p.p.m.[4]

The effect of two substituents X is not necessarily additive. For instance, there is little difference between the positions of the methyl protons in the ethylene ketal of methyl ethyl ketone (I) or acetone dimethyl ketal (II) and the corresponding methyl groups in diethyl ether.

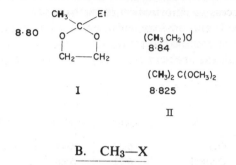

$$8·80$$

$$(CH_3 CH_2)_2 O$$
$$8·84$$

$$(CH_3)_2 C(OCH_3)_2$$
$$8·825$$

I

II

B. CH₃—X

Substituents X attached to the same carbon atom as a proton, or protons, have a profound effect on the resonance frequencies of the latter and consequently we are able to construct very useful correlation tables for these systems.

The α-proton frequencies of simple alkyl halides (X = F, Cl, Br, I) are characteristic of both the halogen and the alkyl group (Table 4.4). The analogous halo-cyclohexane frequencies agree fairly well with those of the acyclic secondary halides, but the cyclopentyl derivatives are all *ca.* 0·30 p.p.m. lower. The origin of the shielding of α-protons in alkyl halides has been discussed by Bothner-By and Naar-Colin[5] in terms of the inductive effect of the halogen and the magnetic anisotropy of the C—X bond. They conclude that both paramagnetic and inter-atomic diamagnetic terms make important contributions to shielding of the α-protons in methyl halides (this effect would be greatest for iodine) but that as the

TABLE 4.4 τ-VALUES OF α-PROTONS IN HALO-ALKANES

X	CH₃X	—CH₂X	>CHX	Cyclo-pentyl	Cyclo-hexyl
F	*5·74*	*5·65*			
Cl	*6·95*	*6·60*	*5·98*	*5·69**	*6·11*
Br	*7·32*	*6·69*	*5·90*	*5·61*	*5·89*
I	*7·84*	*6·86*	*5·80*	*5·66**	*5·66**

* These values are taken from Bothner-By and Naar-Colin.[5] All other values are due to Tiers.

ionic character of the C—X bond is increased by successive alkylation the para-magnetic term diminishes. This is to be expected because the free halide ion, having a spherically symmetrical charge distribution, will be magnetically isotropic. The theory is not completely satisfactory for cyclic compounds and it is probable that factors such as the anisotropies of neighbouring bonds and the variations in bond angles as the size of the halogen is increased, should also be considered. A linear relation between the molecular dipole moments of halo-alkanes and the resonance frequencies of α-protons has been established.[5] Additional α-halogenation causes a further paramagnetic shift but the effect is not additive. Thus, the paramagnetic shifts caused by successive chlorination of methane are 2·82, 2·28, and 1·92 p.p.m.

Hydroxyl, alkoxyl, and acyloxy substituents all produce large shifts. As these are amongst the more common substituents in organic molecules, correlations for protons α to such groups are very important. The appropriate data are assembled in Table 4.5.

TABLE 4.5 PROTONS α TO OXYGEN FUNCTIONS

X	CH₃X	—CH₂X	>CHX
OH	*6·62*	6·44	*6·15*
OAlkyl	6·71	6·60	
OPh	*6·27*	6·10	
O.COAlkyl	6·35	5·90	*4·99*
O.COPh	*6·10*	5·77	*4·88*
O.COCF₃	*6·04*	5·66	

Of particular interest is the paramagnetic shift which is produced by acylation or benzoylation of a hydroxyl group. With primary alcohols this is approximately 0·50 for both acylation and benzoylation. Acylation of secondary alcohols causes the α-proton to move by 1·0–1·15 p.p.m. to lower frequencies, and in steroid molecules this effect is the same for axial and equatorial protons.[4] Thus the assignment of a band in the 5–7 p.p.m. region of the spectrum of an alcohol, to a proton α to hydroxyl is confirmed if the band occurs at lower frequencies in the acyl derivative. Acetylation is to be preferred to benzoylation since the ring current fields of the phenyl group can conceivably change the shielding of other protons in the molecule. The paramagnetic shift caused by trifluoroacetylation is somewhat greater than for acetylation.

The frequencies of the α-protons in alicyclic alcohols and their derivatives vary over a considerable range and are dependent on stereochemistry. In steroids for instance protons attached to the same carbon atoms as hydroxyl groups have frequencies ranging from 5·4 to 6·4. A more detailed analysis of such systems is reserved until Chapter 7.

The frequencies of α-protons in cyclic ethers also differ from their acyclic counterparts. Some examples are given below.

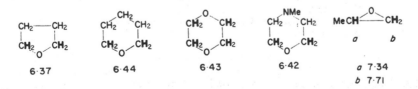

The characteristic shielding of protons in epoxides makes it likely that nuclear magnetic resonance spectroscopy will be widely used for the detection of such groups which, in general, are not readily identified by other physical methods. It is often possible to hydrolyse or reduce epoxides, in which case spectral examination of the product may be used to confirm the original assignment.

The presence of an adjacent nitrogen atom causes a somewhat smaller paramagnetic shift than observed for the oxygen analogues (Table 4.6). Thus, N-methyl groups absorb near 7·8. Spin–spin coupling between the nitrogen nucleus and the methyl protons is very weak, so that N-methyl groups usually give rise to strong (3-proton) sharp signals which can often be recognized even in complex spectra. However, in N-methylpyrrolidine the methylene groups adjacent to nitrogen absorb in the same region so that the assignment of a band at 7·8 to N—Me is not necessarily unambiguous.[7] Furthermore, methyl ketones and O- and N-acetates may also give rise to sharp lines in the same region.

In contrast to N-methylpyrrolidine, most methylene groups adjacent to heterocyclic nitrogen absorb in the range 7·20–7·40 which is somewhat lower than observed for acyclic methylene groups in the same environment. Again, it is apparent that N-acylation causes a paramagnetic shift which can be used to confirm spectral assignments. The spectra of sulphonamides are also useful in this connexion. The paramagnetic shift which accompanies N-acylation is also observed for methylene groups adjacent to nitrogen in lactams as exemplified by a comparison of pyrrolidine (III) with pyrrolidone (IV). Quaternary salt formation also moves the line

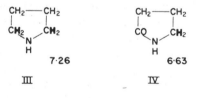

positions of adjacent protons to lower fields. Unfortunately, most salts of this type are insoluble in the recommended organic solvents. Tiers has used trifluoroacetic acid as a solvent for quaternary salts but the invariance of the line positions of internal references in this medium has not yet been established.

TABLE 4.6 ALKYL GROUPS ADJACENT TO NITROGEN

X	CH_3X	$—CH_2X$	$>CHX$
N < (acyclic)	7·85	7·5	7·13
N < (cyclic secondary)		7·3	
N < (cyclic tertiary)	7·80	7·7	
$NH.CO.CH_3$	*7·15*	6·8	
$NH.SO_2.C_6H_4R(R = H,Me)$		6·9	
Quaternary salts	*6·67*	*6·60*	

The frequencies of protons attached to the same carbon atom as a carbonyl group are sufficiently characteristic to be useful in structural work even though the paramagnetic shift caused by the carbonyl group is not as large as for some of the substituents we have considered (Table 4.7). Most methyl groups attached to carbonyl groups give strong (3-proton) lines in the region 7·8–8·05. Methylene and methine group proton frequencies are apparently rather sensitive to ring size. Thus cyclopentanone, cyclohexanone, and cycloheptanone absorb at 7·98, 7·75, and 7·58 respectively. The carbonyl group is known to have a high diamagnetic anisotropy[8] and it is probable that small changes in conformation can result in significant shifts in the frequencies of neighbouring protons. In this connexion it is interesting to note that the α and β protons in cyclopentanone absorb at the same frequency.[9] There is insufficient difference between the shielding produced by the the carbonyl groups in aldehydes, ketones, acids, esters, and amides to enable α-proton frequencies to be used to distinguish between these functions. Alkyl aryl ketones are an exception since the diamagnetic anisotropy of the phenyl group causes a significant paramagnetic shift (Table 4.7).

TABLE 4.7 ALKYL GROUPS ADJACENT TO CARBONYL GROUPS

X	CH₃—X	—CH₂—X	>CH—X
CHO	7·83	7·80	7·61
COAlkyl	7·90	7·60	7·52
COPh	7·38		
CO₂H	7·93	7·66	7·43
CO₂Alkyl	8·00	7·90	
CONH₂	7·98		

Alkyl groups attached to carbon–carbon double bonds usually absorb at slightly higher frequencies than those adjacent to carbonyl groups. Thus methyl groups are generally found in the range 8·05–8·40 (Table 4.8) and a consideration of their frequencies together with those of the associated olefinic protons (see below) may lead to precise structural assignments. It is frequently possible to confirm assignments by hydrogenation of the double bond which causes the methyl frequency to move to the 9·0 region. We shall see in Chapter 6 that the spin–spin coupling constants between allylic protons and α and β olefinic protons are very characteristic and can also be used to determine the orientation of substituents about a double bond. The proton frequencies of methyl groups attached to polyene chains fall into two classes, namely end-of-chain methyl groups (8·2–8·35) and in-chain methyl groups (8·00–8·10).

Small paramagnetic shifts (0·1–0·5 p.p.m.) of allylic proton frequencies are produced by conjugation of the double bond with certain groups (Table 4.8) but as the magnitude of this shift depends on geometric isomerism about the double bond we will defer a detailed discussion of the effect until Chapter 7.

Phenyl substituents cause a much larger paramagnetic shift of alkyl frequencies than either olefinic or carbonyl double bonds (see formulae (V)–(VII)) and there is no doubt that the ring current fields make a major contribution to this deshielding effect. In substituted toluenes only the more powerful electron-withdrawing nuclear substituents significantly alter the frequencies of the methyl group

(Table 4.9), and the effect is greatest in the ortho-positions suggesting the operation of fields arising from the diamagnetic anisotropy of the substituent.

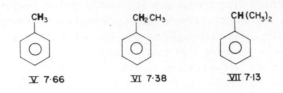

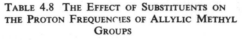

$\underline{V}$ 7·66 $\underline{VI}$ 7·38 $\underline{VII}$ 7·13

TABLE 4.8 THE EFFECT OF SUBSTITUENTS ON
THE PROTON FREQUENCIES OF ALLYLIC METHYL
GROUPS

Compound	Methyl protons
$CH_2:C(CH_3)_2$	8·30
$(CH_3)_2C:CH.CH_3$	8·37
$CH_2:C(CH_3).CHO$	7·90
$(CH_3)_2C:CH.CHO$	8·04, 7·89
$CH_2:C(CH_3).COCH_3$	8·125
$(CH_3)_2C:CH.COCH_3$	8·14, 7·94
$CH_2:C(CH_3).CO_2CH_3$	8·10
$(CH_3)_2C:CH.CO_2CH_3$	8·16, 7·88
$CH_2:C(CH_3).O.COCH_3$	8·09
$(CH_3)_2C:CH.O.COCH_3$	8·35
$CH_2:C(CH_3).C\vdots CH$	8·11
$(CH_3)_2C:CH.C\vdots CH$	8·24, 8·14
$CH_2:C(CH_3).Ph$	7·86
$CH_2:C(CH_3).CN$	7·97
$CH_2:C(CH_3).Br$	7·70
$(CH_3)_2C:CH.Br$	8·25
$CH_2:C(CH_3).CH:CH_2$	8·16
β-Carotene (end-of-chain)	8·31
β-Carotene (in-chain)	8·055

TABLE 4.9. THE EFFECT OF NUCLEAR SUBSTITUENTS
ON THE PROTON FREQUENCY OF THE METHYL GROUP
IN TOLUENE

Substituent	o	m	p
Nil	(7·66)	(7·66)	(7·66)
MeO			7·75
OH	7·71	7·73	7·70
$CH_3CO.O$			7·68
$(CH_3)_2CH$			7·73
Me	7·71	7·73	7·70
$PhCH_2$			7·73
F			7·70
$CO.CH_3$			7·60
CO_2Me	7·15	7·73	7·48
NO_2	7·47	7·58	7·57

Alkyl groups attached to polycyclic aromatic systems are expected to have frequencies in much the same region as the analogous derivatives of benzene but no accurate data are available.

4.3 THE ADDITIVITY OF SUBSTITUENT EFFECTS —SHOOLERY'S RULES

In section 4.2 we summarized the effective shielding of alkyl protons by a substituent X in different environments, but frequently we have to consider shielding by more than one substituent. Shoolery[11] of Varian Associates has developed a procedure for calculating the alkyl proton frequencies in acyclic systems. The method is highly successful for systems of the type $Y—CH_2—X$ but rather unreliable for the type

$$Y—\overset{\displaystyle \overset{X}{|}}{C}H—Z.$$

Dailey and Shoolery,[12] in 1955, established a close relation between the electronegativity of a substituent X and the shielding of neighbouring protons. However, we cannot develop additivity relations on this fact alone since the electron withdrawal from a carbon atom becomes more difficult as the number of electron withdrawing substituents is increased. To overcome this difficulty Shoolery has taken the averages of the shifts caused by successive substitutions of methane by X as the effective shielding constant of X (cf. p. 55). He has pointed out that the values so obtained lie between the values for the first and second substitutions, being somewhat nearer the latter. The effective shielding constants ($\sigma_i^{eff.}$) of various substituents are listed in Table 4.10. One or two extra values have been added to Shoolery's

TABLE 4.10. SHOOLERY'S EFFECTIVE
SHIELDING CONSTANTS

Group	$\sigma_{ieff.}$ (p.p.m.)
Cl	2·53
Br	2·33
I	1·82
NR^1R^2	1·57
OR	2·36
SR	1·64
CR = O	1·70
$CR^1 = CR^2R^3$	1·32
C ≡ CH	1·44
C ≡ N	1·70
CH_3	0·47

original list. The shielding constants may be used in conjunction with equation (1) to calculate the expected positions of methylene and methine protons in which

$$\tau\text{-alkyl} = 9·767 - \sum_i \sigma_{i_{eff.}}. \tag{1}$$

τ-alkyl is the proton frequency in the system $X^1—CH_2—X^2$ or $X^1—\overset{\displaystyle \overset{X^2}{|}}{C}H—X^3$ and

$\sigma_i^{eff,}$ is the effective shielding constant of X^i. The term 9·767 is the τ-value of methane. Equation (1) has been found to reproduce the τ-values of some twenty methylene protons with an average deviation of $\pm 0·05$ p.p.m. (Table 4.11). The calculated values of methine protons are much less satisfactory.

Shoolery's constants apply only to acyclic systems and apparently only to methylene groups. Even with these limitations the procedure is extremely valuable and is likely to be widely used.

TABLE 4.11 COMPARISON OF PREDICTED AND
OBSERVED SHIELDING VALUES IN SUBSTITUTED
METHANES

Compound type	Calculated	Observed
$Br—CH_2—Cl$	4·89	4·84
$C_6H_5—CH_2—Cl$	5·39	5·49
$C_6H_5—CH_2—OR$	5·56	5·59
$C_6H_5—CH_2—Br$	5·59	5·58
$(Cl—CH_2—C=)_2$	5·91	5·96
$—CH=CH—CH_2—OH$	6·08	6·09
$CH_2=CH—CH_2—Br$	6·11	6·14
$C_6H_5—CH_2—C\overset{O}{\diagdown}$	6·22	6·21
$C_6H_5—CH_2—N<$	6·36	6·44
$=C—CH_2—C\overset{O}{\diagdown}$	6·74	6·84
$CH_3—CH_2—OR$	6·84	6·63
$CH_3—CH_2—C_6H_5$	7·38	7·38
$CH_3—CH_2—C\overset{O}{\diagdown}$	7·51	7·61
$CH_3—CH_2—S—$	7·58	7·61
$CH_3—CH_2—N<$	7·64	7·58
$I—CH_2—I$	6·99	5·91
$Cl—CH_2—Cl$	4·69	4·66
$Br—CH_2—Br$	5·09	5·06
$C_6H_5—CH_2—C_6H_5$	6·09	6·08
$=C—CH_2—C=$	7·13	7·09
$Cl—CH_2—I$	5·41	5·01

4.4 OLEFINIC, ALLENIC, AND ACETYLENIC PROTONS

Some of the earliest structural applications of nuclear magnetic resonance spectroscopy involved the detection of olefinic protons, and certainly the method is capable of yielding precise information concerning the numbers and environments of olefinic protons even in complex molecules.

Olefinic proton frequencies lie in the region 2·0–5·5. The reduced shielding of such protons must depend on a large paramagnetic term associated with the π-electron system as well as on the increased electron-withdrawal by the sp^2 hybridized carbon atoms. In non-conjugated hydrocarbons olefinic proton frequencies fall between 4·3 and 5·4 and the exact position gives some indication of the number and orientation of substituents (Table 4.12). Rather more precise correlations should become possible as more data accumulate. In acyclic systems, conjugation with other carbon–carbon double bonds can cause a paramagnetic shift (*ca.* 0·50 p.p.m.).

TABLE 4.12 OLEFINIC PROTONS IN HYDROCARBONS

Type	Unconjugated	Conjugated
Terminal methylene	5·35	5·10
Non-terminal acyclic	4·45–4·95	3·6–4·2
Cyclic	4·10–4·70	4·1–4·6
Terminal allenic	*5·6*	
Allenic	*5·2*	
Acetylenic	7·65	7·30

Allenic protons appear to absorb at frequencies higher by 0·3 p.p.m. than those of analogous olefins, although few examples are available.[2] The position of acetylenic protons (7·65) is the result of a compromise between the inductive ($-I$) and diamagnetic anisotropy (p. 17) effects of the carbon–carbon triple bond.

Substituents, particularly those which enter into conjugation with a double bond, can cause fairly large shifts in olefinic proton frequencies. Some examples are given in Table 4.13. The exact position of the β-proton absorption often

TABLE 4.13 THE EFFECT OF SUBSTITUENTS ON
OLEFINIC PROTON FREQUENCIES

Compound	α-Proton	β-Protons
$CH_2:C(CH_3)_2$	—	5·34
$(CH_3)_2C:CH.CH_3$	4·79	—
$CH_2:C(CH_3).CHO$	—	3·925, 3·625
$(CH_3)_2.C:CH.CHO$	4·15	—
$CH_2:C(CH_3).COCH_3$	—	4·08, 3·88
$(CH_3)_2C:CH.COCH_3$	4·03	—
$CH_2:C(CH_3)CO_2CH_3$	—	3·97, 4·51
$(CH_3)_2C:CH.CO_2CH_3$	4·38	—
$CH_2:C(CH_3).O.COCH_3$	—	5·38
$(CH_3)_2C:CH.O.COCH_3$	3·21	—
$(CH_3)_2C:CH.C:CH$	4·83	—
$CH_2:C(CH_3).Ph$	—	4·98, 4·72
$CH_2:C(CH_3).CN$	—	4·22, 4·28
$(CH_3)_2C:CH.Br$	4·22	—

depends on geometric isomerism, as will be seen in Chapter 7. Furthermore, the effect of conjugation will also depend on the ability of the system to adopt the correct conformation for maximum conjugation and consequently we may expect that nuclear magnetic resonance will prove to be a useful technique for studying the steric inhibition of conjugation.

Attention is drawn to the positions of the olefinic proton bands in the two cyclic enol ethers (VIII) and (IX) as they are to some extent anomalous.

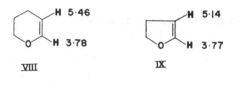

VIII   IX

4.5 ALDEHYDIC PROTONS

The anomalous shielding of aldehydic protons was discussed in Chapter 2 (p. 17). Because of the unique line position (0·0–0·7) of the aldehydic proton, nuclear magnetic resonance spectroscopy provides a most convenient method of detecting the aldehyde function. Aliphatic aldehydes usually give a band near 0·35. α:β-Unsaturation produces a small diamagnetic shift (0·1–0·2 p.p.m.) whereas aromatic substituents cause shifts (0·25–0·35) to lower fields.

Curtin and his co-workers[14] have shown that a distinction between aldehydes and ketones can also be made from a consideration of the nuclear magnetic resonance spectra of their semicarbazones and 2:4-dinitrophenylhydrazones. Semicarbazones of aldehydes give bands in the region 2·2–2·6 and the 2:4-dinitrophenylhydrazones absorb between 2·8 and 3·2. These bands are absent in the spectra of the corresponding derivatives of ketones.

4.6 AROMATIC PROTONS IN HYDROCARBONS AND HETEROCYCLES

The various theoretical methods (p. 18) which are used to derive the internuclear diamagnetic effect to the shielding of aromatic protons, yield reasonable results for benzenoid aromatic hydrocarbons but are less satisfactory for nonbenzenoid types such as azulene. If the unequal charge distribution of π-electrons in azulene is taken into account the agreement with experiment is improved.[15] In practice the spectra of the larger polycyclic systems are of limited value in structural work since they give rise to one or more broad band envelopes in the region 1·0 to 3·0.[16]

The aromatic proton frequencies of substituted benzenes fall between 2·0 and 3·5 according to the number and nature of the substituents. Corio and Dailey[18] have examined a number of monosubstituted benzenes and their data are summarized in Table 4.14.* We may notice that certain types of substituents give rise to different shielding at the *ortho*, *meta*, and *para* positions. There is a rough correlation between the frequency shifts relative to benzene and the factors which govern orientation of substituents and activation of the aromatic nucleus in electrophilic aromatic substitution. One notable feature is the abnormal shielding of the

*For many compounds the chemical shifts quoted by Corio and Dailey are only approximate since detailed analyses (p. 89) of the spectra were not carried out.

ortho positions by some substituents. In nitrobenzene, for instance, the frequencies of the *meta* and *para* protons are nearly the same whereas the *ortho* protons are found at a frequency which is lower by 0·6 p.p.m. This has been ascribed to the operation of the inductive effect at the *ortho* position.[18] Such an explanation does not agree with the currently accepted theories of the role of the inductive effect in the determination of the *ortho–para* ratio in electrophilic substitution.[19] For instance, the specific *ortho* deshielding does not occur with cyano or halogen substituents and yet these substituents are known to have inductive effects large enough to influence the *ortho–para* ratio. Corio and Dailey have suggested that the *ortho–para* ratio is determined by the inductomeric rather than the inductive effect and

TABLE 4.14 THE EFFECT OF SUBSTITUTION ON THE PROTON FREQUENCY (2·73) OF BENZENE

Substituent	Shifts relative to Benzene (p.p.m.)		
	ortho	*meta*	*para*
NO_2	−0·97	−0·30	−0·42
CHO	−0·73	−0·23	−0·37
COCl	−0·90	−0·23	−0·30
CO_2CH_3	−0·93	−0·20	−0·27
$COCH_3$	−0·63	−0·27	−0·27
CN	−0·30	−0·30	−0·30
CO_2H	−0·63	−0·10	−0·17
CCl_3	−0·80	−0·17	−0·23
$CHCl_2$	−0·13	−0·13	−0·13
CH_2Cl	0·00	0·00	0·00
CH_3	0·10	0·10	0·10
CH_2CH_3	0·07	0·07	0·07
CH_2OH	0·07	0·07	0·07
CH_2NH_2	0·03	0·03	0·03
Cl	0·00	0·00	0·00
Br	0·0	0·0	0·0
I	−0·30	0·17	0·10
OCH_3	0·23	0·23	0·23
OH	0·37	0·37	0·37
NH_2	0·77	0·13	0·40
$NH(CH_3)$	0·80	0·30	0·57
$N(CH_3)_2$	0·50	0·20	0·50

that there is no basis for a comparison between the former and magnetic shielding. However, the fact remains that the nitro and cyano groups have almost the same dipole moment in both aliphatic and aromatic systems indicating a comparable polarizability for the two groups. It seems more reasonable to relate the anomalous *ortho* shielding to the diamagnetic anisotropy of the substituent or even to incipient hydrogen-bonding between the *ortho* hydrogen atom and the substituent. A closely related problem is the origin of the differential shielding of *cis* and *trans* protons in ethylenic systems (see Chapter 7).

The introduction of a hetero-atom into an aromatic ring system causes much larger shifts than the substituent effects which we have just discussed. The complicated spectrum of pyridine has been completely analysed[20] and the τ-values are given in (X).

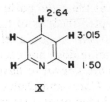

X

In general, aromatic protons adjacent to a hetero-atom absorb at lower frequencies than those in other positions. This effect, which is probably electrostatic in origin, is most marked when the hetero-atom is either oxygen or nitrogen as in pyrrole (XI) or furan (XII). The α- and β-protons in thiophene (XIII) are almost equally shielded.

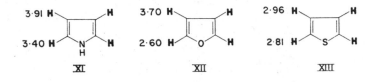

XI   XII   XIII

Corey and his co-workers[21] have examined a number of furan derivatives (Table 4.15) and have confirmed that limonin, the chief bitter principle of citrus, contains a β-substituted furan ring. They substantiated their assignments by examining the spectrum of tetrahydrolimonin in which the appropriate bands were found to be absent.

TABLE 4.15 PROTON FREQUENCIES* OF FURAN:
THE EFFECT OF SUBSTITUTION

Substituents	α-Proton (s)	β-Proton (s)
Nil	2·60	3·70
2-Me	2·82	3·85, 4·12
2:5-Me$_2$	—	4·20
2-OH	2·52	3·67
2-CHO	2·17	2·67, 3·30
2-CO$_2$H	2·52	2·425, 3·20
3-CO$_2$H	2·12, 2·70	3·40

* Extrapolated from Corey's values which were obtained using water as an external reference.

The effect of substitution in the thiophene nucleus has been studied by Gronowitz and Hoffman[22] and their results are summarized in Table 4.16.

It seems probable that many aromatic heterocycles may give characteristic nuclear magnetic resonance spectra but a survey of the more common types is not

TABLE 4.16. PROTON FREQUENCIES OF THIOPHENE:
THE EFFECT OF SUBSTITUTION

Substituent	Ring Proton			
	2	3	4	5
2-NO$_2$	—	2·31	2·89	2·41
2-OCH$_3$	—	3·89	3·41	4·14
2-COCH$_3$	—	2·36	2·90	2·36
2-CHO	—	2·31	2·86	2·21
2-CO$_2$H	—	2·29	2·89	2·29
2-SO$_2$CH$_3$	—	2·21	2·84	2·21
3-COCH$_3$	1·66	—	2·26	2·46
3-SO$_2$CH$_3$	1·74	—	2·56	2·44
3-OCH$_3$	3·92	—	3·34	3·06
3-SCH$_3$	3·09	—	3·09	2·86
3-CO$_2$H	1·81	—	2·56	2·56
3-CHO	1·84	—	2·31	2·31
3-CH$_3$	3·31	—	2·31	2·06

yet available in the literature. It has been shown that the proton spectra of glyoxaline and pyrazole are sufficiently characteristic to permit a distinction between the two ring systems, and this fact has been used to establish the presence of the pyrazole ring in a new plant amino-acid isolated from water-melon seeds.[23]

REFERENCES

1. L. H. MEYER, A. SAIKA and H. S. GUTOWSKY, *J. Am. Chem. Soc.* **75**, 1567 (1953).
2. N. F. CHAMBERLAIN, *Anal. Chem.* **31**, 56 (1959).
3. G. VAN DYKE TIERS, Private communication.
4. J. N. SHOOLERY and M. T. ROGERS. *J. Am. Chem. Soc.* **80**, 5121 (1958).
5. A. A. BOTHNER-BY and C. NAAR-COLIN, *ibid.* 1728.
6. A. A. BOTHNER-BY and C. NAAR-COLIN, *Ann. New York. Acad Sci.* **70**, 833 (1958).
7. H. CONROY, P. R. BROOK, M. K. ROUT and N. SILVERMAN, *J. Am. Chem. Soc.* **80**, 5178 (1958).
8. J. A. POPLE, *Proc. Roy. Soc.* A239, 550 (1957).
9. H. PRIMAS, K. FREI and H. H. GUNTHARD, *Helv. Chem. Acta.* **41**, 34 (1958).
10. M. S. BARBER, L. M. JACKMAN and B. C. L. WEEDON, *Proc. Chem. Soc.* 96 (1959), and unpublished results.
11. J. N. SHOOLERY, *Technical Information Bulletin*, Varian Associates, Palo Alto, California, 2, No. 3 (1959).
12. B. P. DAILEY and J. N. SHOOLERY, *J. Am. Chem. Soc.* **77**, 3977 (1955).
13. L. M. JACKMAN and R. H. WILEY, Unpublished results.
14. D. Y. CURTIN, J. A. GOURSE, W. H. RICHARDSON and K. L. RINEHART, Jr. *J. Org. Chem.* **24**, 93 (1959).
15. W. G. SCHNEIDER, H. J. BERNSTEIN and J. A. POPLE, *J. Am. Chem. Soc.* **80**, 3497 (1958).
16. H. J. BERNSTEIN and W. G. SCHNEIDER, *J. Chem. Phys.* **24**, 468 (1956).
17. J. S. WAUGH and R. W. FESSENDEN, *J. Am. Chem. Soc.* **79**, 846 (1957).
18. P. L. CORIO and B. P. DAILEY, *ibid.* **78**, 3043 (1956).
19. C. K. INGOLD, *Structure and Mechanism in Organic Chemistry*, Bell, London, 19, p. 16.
20. W. G. SCHNEIDER, H. J. BERNSTEIN and J. A. POPLE, *Ann. New York Acad. Sci.* **70**, 806 (1958); *Canad. J. Chem.* **35**, 1487 (1957).
21. E. J. COREY, G. SLOMP, S. DEV, S. TOBINAGA, and E. R. GLAZIER, *J. Am. Chem. Soc.* **80**, 1204 (1958).
22. S. GRONOWITZ and R. A. HOFFMAN, *Arkiv. Kemi*, **13**, 279 (1958).
23. L. FOWDEN, F. F. NOE, J. H. RIDD and R. F. M. WHITE, *Proc. Chem. Soc.* 131 (1959).

CHAPTER 5

THE CORRELATION OF CHEMICAL SHIFTS WITH MOLECULAR STRUCTURE (*cont.*)

IN THIS chapter we shall discuss chemical shifts of various elements, including hydrogen in certain molecular environments, for which precise correlations with molecular structure either cannot or have not been established, but which may from time to time assume importance in structural organic chemistry.

A. PROTONS ATTACHED TO ELEMENTS OTHER THAN CARBON

5.1 HYDROGEN ATTACHED TO OXYGEN

The resonance frequencies (τ-values) of protons attached to oxygen are extremely sensitive to *intermolecular* environment and are therefore less readily correlated with molecular structure than the frequencies of those types discussed in the previous chapter. When we consider the frequencies of alcoholic hydroxyl, phenolic hydroxyl, enolic hydroxyl, and carboxylic hydroxyl protons in relation to molecular structure we have to bear in mind two phenomena which can alter the apparent shielding of such protons. These two phenomena are intermolecular hydrogen-bonding and chemical exchange.

The marked effect of hydrogen-bonding on the resonance frequencies of protons was established at a very early stage in the development of nuclear magnetic resonance.[1,2] Hydrogen-bonding causes a very large paramagnetic shift (6 to 7 p.p.m.) the origin of which has been discussed by Schneider, Bernstein and Pople[3] in terms of the simple electrostatic picture of the hydrogen-bond.

A number of studies of hydrogen bonding in liquids have been reported.[4-13] We shall discuss several of these since they will provide us with an idea of the magnitude of the effect and indicate the way in which we have to proceed if we are to obtain information regarding molecular structure. Saunders and Hyne[11] have carried out a careful study of methanol, *tert.*-butanol and phenol as the pure liquids and as solutions in carbon tetrachloride. In all cases the hydroxylic and phenolic protons give rise to single absorption bands, the positions of which were dependent on the concentrations of the alcohols or phenol. Their results are summarized graphically in Fig. 5.1. The shape of the concentration vs. chemical shift curves were shown to be consistent with an equilibrium system involving monomeric alcohol and a trimeric hydrogen bonded complex. We may draw the following useful conclusions from these results. Firstly, the equilibrium between monomer and complex must be established very rapidly for otherwise the monomer and complex would have given rise to separate absorption bands (p. 28). Secondly, the resonance frequencies of the monomers can only be obtained by a rather careful extrapolation to infinite dilution. Finally, it appears likely that the hydroxyl frequencies of the monomers at infinite dilution in carbon tetrachloride will prove

66

to be characteristic of the intramolecular environment of the —OH group. Thus, frequency of the hydroxylic proton of *tert.*-butanol is only 0·10 p.p.m. lower than that of methanol, a frequency difference which is comparable with that observed for the methyl protons of neopentane and ethane.

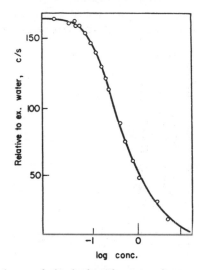

Fig. 5.1 The dependence of the hydroxyl proton frequency of *tert.*-butanol on concentration in CCl₄ (40 Mc.).
(After M. Saunders and J. B. Hyne[11].)

As the monomer–trimer equilibrium has an appreciable enthalpy the hydroxyl proton frequencies will be temperature sensitive.[2]

The observed frequency of a hydroxylic proton in a monomer is dependent on the nature of the solvent. This was first demonstrated by Cohen and Reid[7] who determined the frequencies of monomeric water in three solvents (see Table 5.1). Gränacher[12] has plotted the hydroxylic proton frequency of phenol as a function

TABLE 5.1[7] PROTON FREQUENCIES OF MONOMERIC
WATER IN VARIOUS SOLVENTS

Solvent	Limiting frequency (c/s) relative to cyclohexane
Chloroform	−3
Carbon tetrachloride	+18
Benzene	+38

of concentration in several solvents and her results are reproduced in Fig. 5.2. As with water the limiting frequency varies with the solvent. It is apparent that the interaction of basic solvents with the hydroxyl groups causes a paramagnetic shift the magnitude of which will depend partly on the strength of the hydrogen bond between the solvent and hydroxyl group. However, the data in Table 5.1 and Fig. 5.2 suggest that aromatic solvents cause a diamagnetic shift which Gränacher has suggested is also a consequence of hydrogen bonding. In this case the normal paramagnetic effect is overshadowed by a shielding associated with the diamagnetic anisotropy of the aromatic nucleus[12a] (p. 18). We may therefore conclude that the hydroxyl proton frequencies of a monomeric alcohol in various solvents are not necessarily a measure of the strengths of the solvent–alcohol hydrogen bonds.

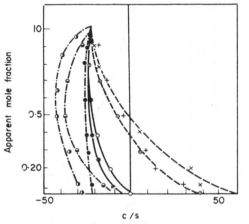

FIG. 5.2   The dependence of the hydroxyl proton frequency (at 32·4 Mc.; uncorrected
for bulk susceptibility) on concentration and the nature of the solvent.

◐	Tetrahydrofuran	⊗	Cyclohexane	⊙	Benzene
⊖	Et$_2$O	○	Carbon disulphide	+	Chlorobenzene
●	(CH$_3$)$_2$CO; CH$_3$CO$_2$Et.			×	Thiophene

(after J. Gränacher[12])

An important point emerges from the work of Huggins, Pimentel, and Shoolery.[6] These authors studied the variation with concentration of the hydroxylic proton frequencies of several phenols in carbon tetrachloride solution and their results are summarized in Table 5.2. The frequencies at infinite dilution of the first four phenols listed in the table agree fairly closely whereas that of *o*-chlorophenol is shifted to a value lower by approximately 1·0 p.p.m. Furthermore, in contrast to the other phenols, the rate of change of τ with concentration [$(d\tau/dX)_{x=0}$] at infinite dilution observed for *o*-chlorophenol is zero. Evidently *o*-chlorophenol is subject to *intramolecular* hydrogen bonding as shown in (I), and hence exists in the monomeric state at concentrations for which the other phenols are still partially polymerized. This observation suggests that we can use the shape of the hydroxylic proton frequency vs. concentration curve to identify intramolecular hydrogen bonding. Presumably some information about strength of an intramolecular bond can be obtained from the monomer frequency, although, as in the case of solvent interaction discussed above, other shielding mechanisms must be taken into account. Because of the magnitude of the shifts associated with hydrogen bonding, nuclear magnetic resonance spectroscopy will doubtless prove to be a valuable alternative to infrared spectroscopy for the investigation of structural features which permit such an interaction.

We now turn to a consideration of chemical exchange, the general principles of which were outlined in Chapter 2 (p. 28). The example of the acid-catalyzed proton exchange between water and ethanol is instructive for it shows that the line position of the hydroxyl proton is dependent on the relative concentrations of water and ethanol. Indeed, the line position of this signal can be used to estimate relative concentrations. If we wish to study hydroxyl proton frequencies in relation to chemical structure we must always bear in mind the possibility of exchange. Thus polyfunctional compounds such as diols, hydroxy acids etc. may give anomalous results if proton exchange occurs and solvents which have readily exchangeable protons (e.g. alcohols, acids, and primary and secondary amines) should be avoided.

TABLE 5.2[6] HYDROGEN-BONDING OF PHENOLS IN CARBON TETRACHLORIDE AS A FUNCTION OF CONCENTRATION
(X = apparent mole fraction)

Compound	$\tau_{x=1}$	$\tau_{x=0}$	$(d\tau/dX)_{x=0}$
Phenol	3·0	5·8	42
o-Cresol	3·4	5·5	16
p-Chlorophenol	3·0	5·3	20
m-Chlorophenol	3·0	5·5	22
o-Chlorophenol	3·7	4·4	0·0

I

We are now in a position to outline the main features of hydroxyl proton resonance in the principal classes of hydroxylic compounds.

Alcohols

The hydroxyl frequencies of alcohols can vary over a wide range according to the nature of the solvent, concentration of solute and temperature. In carbon tetrachloride the hydroxylic proton frequencies of monomeric alcohol are near 9·5. No examples of intramolecular hydrogen bonding have been reported but it is probable that such bonding can be recognized from the shapes of frequency vs. concentration curves, and that useful correlations between monomer frequencies and the strengths of the intramolecular hydrogen bond can be established for certain classes of compounds.

Phenols

As in the case of alcohols the observed frequencies are determined by concentration, solvent, and temperature. Monomer frequencies are found near 5·5 in cyclohexane and in carbon tetrachloride. There is evidence that intramolecular hydrogen bonding is associated with a large paramagnetic shift (see Table 5.3).

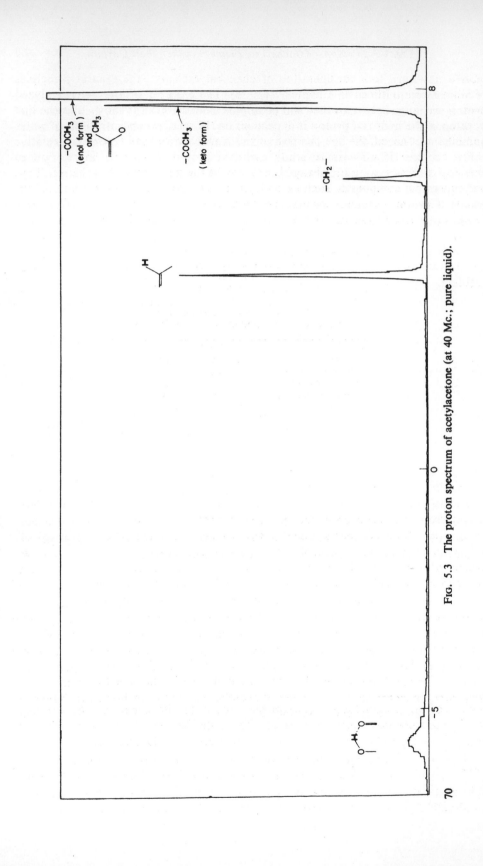

Fig. 5.3 The proton spectrum of acetylacetone (at 40 Mc.; pure liquid).

Enols

Since most stable enols owe their existence to strong intramolecular hydrogen bonding we may expect that they will be largely monomeric and that their hydroxylic protons will absorb at very low frequencies. Several groups of workers have examined acetylacetone.[14-17] The frequency of the hydroxylic proton is very low ($-5\cdot4$) and has the same value in acetic acid and triethylamine solutions as in the pure liquid. This suggests a negligible solvent interaction. In acetic acid at room temperature separate peaks are observed for the enolic and carboxylic protons. As these signals are broad and coalesce at 64 °C it is evident that the chemical exchange of protons is just becoming important at room temperature. Acetylacetone, as a pure liquid, is a 4:1 mixture of the enol and keto forms. The room temperature spectrum (Fig. 5.3) exhibits absorption characteristic of both forms indicating that the rate of interconversion of the two isomers is too slow to effect an average shielding.

TABLE 5.3 INTRAMOLECULAR HYDROGEN-BONDING
IN PHENOLS

Compound (in cyclohexane)	Monomer frequency τ
Phenol	5·76
o-Chlorophenol	4·40
Methyl salicylate	−0·58
Salicylaldehyde	−0·95

Carboxylic Acids

The behaviour of carboxylic acids in non-polar solvents (e.g. CCl_4) differs sharply from that of alcohols and phenols in that carboxylic proton frequencies are invariant with concentration.[6,7] This is a result of the known tendency of carboxylic acids to form stable dimers. Aliphatic carboxylic acids in carbon tetrachloride absorb near $-0\cdot8$. In polar aprotic solvents, particularly those which can act as proton acceptors, the dimers are less stable and the carboxylic proton frequencies are concentration dependent. Carboxylic acids enter into a rapid proton exchange with hydroxylic solvents so that the two types of —OH groups give rise to one sharp line, the position of which depends on the relative concentrations of solvent and solute.

Because of the great variation of the frequencies of protons in various types of —OH groups it is often impossible, on the basis of line position, to identify their signals in the spectrum of a complex molecule. Although the —OH frequency may be of no interest there is always the danger that its signal may be wrongly assigned to some other structural feature. This difficulty can be overcome in several ways. The temperature or concentration dependence of the frequencies of many types of hydroxylic protons may be used to identify their signals in complex spectra. If the hydroxyl frequency is of no interest the best procedure is to replace the appropriate hydrogen atom by deuterium which can usually be effected by merely shaking the sample with deuterium oxide.

5.2 HYDROGEN ATTACHED TO NITROGEN

Many of the features of the magnetic resonance of protons attached to oxygen are also exhibited by the nitrogen analogues. However, a further complication arises from the fact that ^{14}N possesses an electric quadruple moment.

Three types of signals have been observed for protons attached to nitrogen, namely single sharp lines, broad bands, or triplets.[18]

The nitrogen nucleus (^{14}N) has a spin of unity ($I = 1$) so that in theory the absorption line of a proton attached to it will be split by spin–spin coupling into three components of equal intensity. This behaviour has been observed for rigorously purified ammonia[19,20] and for amines in acid solution,[18,21] the magnitude of the splitting (J_{HN}) being 50–60 c/s. Many amides and pyrrole on the other hand give broad singlets. In some cases the bands are so broad as to be almost unobservable. There are two conceivable explanations for this phenomenon. Firstly, the nitrogen quadrupole could shorten the spin–lattice relaxation time to a value comparable with the reciprocal of the spin–spin coupling constant J_{HN} (cf. p. 13). Alternatively, there is the possibility of a proton exchange occurring with a frequency comparable with J_{HN}. That the former is the correct explanation follows from the work of Roberts[18] in which he has shown that broad amide bands revert to triplets at elevated temperatures. If chemical exchange had been the cause of broadening, a narrow singlet would have been observed since the rate of exchange would necessarily have increased with temperature so causing spin–spin coupling to average to a single value.

Free amines give rise to a single sharp absorption line.* This behaviour is consistent with rapid chemical exchange of the amino hydrogen atoms. This exchange is inhibited by protonation of the amine so that the appearance of signals from amino hydrogen atoms in aqueous media is dependent on the pH of the solution. This is well illustrated by the spectra of methylamine in aqueous solutions of varying pH.[21] In highly acid solutions (Fig. 5.4A) exchange is effectively suppressed and the amine exists as $(CH_3NH_3)^+$. Accordingly, the methyl group signal is split as a quartet by coupling with the three protons attached to the nitrogen atom. The $—NH_3$ protons give rise to a triplet ($J_{HN} \sim 50$ c/s) since they are coupled to the nitrogen atom. This band is too broad to permit the observation of the smaller splitting caused by the adjacent methyl group. At lower acidities proton exchange between water and the amine sets in. This is first observed as a broadening of the water and amino group signals and at the same time the fine structure of the methyl group signal disappears (Fig. 5.4B). These conditions correspond to an intermediate exchange rate. A further increase in pH raises the exchange rate to a value well above the reciprocals of the separations of the various lines in the spectrum so that now the signals of the amino group and of water coalesce to a single sharp line. The coupling between the methyl and amino protons is averaged to zero so that the methyl group also gives rise to a single sharp absorption line (Fig. 5.4C).

We have seen that quadrupole relaxation is more effective in amides than in ammonium salts. In fact the relaxation in certain N-acylamino acids is so efficient that the $—CONH—$ groups give rise to quite sharp singlets.[22] We saw in Chapter 2

---

*Whether this is true of all types of amines, especially under completely anhydrous conditions, cannot be stated with certainty (cf. ref. 19).

that quadrupole relaxation involves the interaction of the nuclear quadrupole with fluctuating electric field gradients. The principal contribution will arise from asymmetric fields which immediately surround the nucleus since rotations of the molecule will cause such fields to exert a torque on the nucleus. In the ammonium and alkylammonium cations the electric fields surrounding the nitrogen nucleus have a high symmetry and consequently the torque to which the latter is subjected is small and the relaxation time, T_1, fairly long. The sp^2 hybridization of the nitrogen orbitals in amides and pyrrole lowers the symmetry of the field around the nitrogen nucleus and results in a decreased relaxation time.

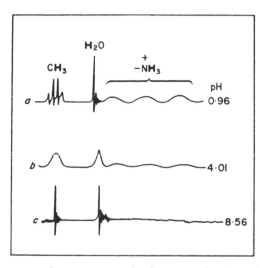

FIG. 5.4   Proton spectra of aqueous methylamine at varying pH. The water signal has been recorded at reduced amplification. (After E. Grunwald, A. Loewerstein, and S. Meiboom[21]).

As yet, the frequencies of protons attached to nitrogen have received little attention. Chamberlain gives the following ranges: aliphatic and cyclic amines, 5·0–8·1; aromatic amines, 5·3–6·4; amides 2·0–5·0. These figures are based on measurements in a variety of solvents. Doubtless $>$ NH proton frequencies are influenced by hydrogen bonding but no data for monomer frequencies in inert solvents are available.

The determination of amido and pyrrolic proton frequencies is greatly hampered by the broadness of the signals. The bands can be sharpened considerably by catalyzing the proton exchange. This has been done in the case of pyrrole by adding sodium to the sample (the catalyst is the pyrrole anion, $C_4H_4N^-$)[18] and proton exchange in amides is subject to both acid and base catalysis.[23] However, such methods do not lend themselves to studies in solvents which are suitable for the determination of accurate shielding values (p. 46). The removal of the undesirable broadening of the $>$NH resonance is best effected by use of the spin decoupling (double resonance) technique referred to in Chapter 2 (p. 25). The spectra of pyrrole with and without irradiation at the resonance frequency of the ^{14}N nucleus are illustrated in Figs. 5.5A and B. The result of double irradiation is quite dramatic since the $>$NH band in the normal spectrum is so broad as to be invisible whereas under double resonance conditions the band appears as a partially resolved triplet, the fine structure resulting from coupling with the α-hydrogen atoms. The technique of spin-decoupling will prove invaluable for nuclear magnetic resonance investigations of the structures of amides.

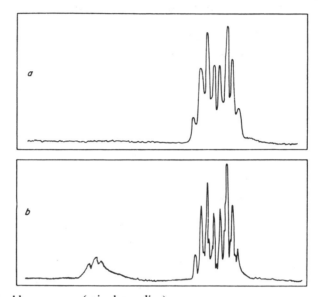

FIG. 5.5   Double resonance (spin decoupling)
(a) Proton spectrum of pyrrole.
(b) Proton spectrum of pyrrole with ^{14}N irradiated at its resonance frequency
(from N.M.R. at Work, Varian Associates[24]).

5.3 PROTONS IN THIOLS AND METAL HYDRIDES

Few examples of the nuclear magnetic resonance of thiolic protons are available.[13,25,26] Chamberlain[13] gives the range 8·4–8·8 for aliphatic thiols and the value 6·4 for thiophenol (—SH). The extent of hydrogen bonding of thiols has not been established so that we do not know for certain that these values refer to monomeric —SH.

Hydrogen attached to heavy elements generally appears to be strongly shielded presumably as the result of a large paramagnetic term associated with the heavy atom. Transition metal hydrides give lines in the region 17·5–30·0 and nuclear magnetic resonance spectroscopy has proved very useful for establishing the structures of organometallic hydrides in which the problem is often that of distinguishing between carbon–hydrogen and metal–hydrogen bonds.[24]

B. NUCLEAR MAGNETIC RESONANCE OF ISOTOPES OTHER THAN ^{1}H

It is apparent from our discussions of proton chemical shifts that the fields arising from local diamagnetic, neighbouring paramagnetic, and interatomic diamagnetic currents (p. 16) can make comparable contributions to the shielding of the hydrogen nucleus whereas the paramagnetic term associated with hydrogen itself is negligible. When we turn to the nuclear magnetic resonance of other nuclei we find that the paramagnetic term associated with the nucleus under observation is overwhelmingly important. This was shown to be the case by Saika and Slichter[28] in a classic paper dealing with the theoretical calculation of fluorine chemical shifts. They established a relation between the paramagnetic term, which vanishes for the spherically symmetrical fluoride ion, and the covalent character of the F—X bond. Their theory predicts that the shielding of the fluorine nucleus decreases as the electro-negativity of X is increased. The chemical shifts for other elements probably have a similar origin although complications will arise with those elements which can exhibit polyvalency. The range of shifts observed for fluorine and other elements are usually an order of magnitude greater than for hydrogen.

Table 5.4 lists the magnetic properties of those nuclei which are of greatest interest to organic chemists.

5.4. FLUORINE (^{19}F)

The resonance frequency of the fluorine nucleus is slightly lower than hydrogen ($\nu_H \sim 40$ Mc and $\nu_F \sim 37\cdot65$ at 9400 gauss) and fluorine nuclear magnetic resonance absorption can be readily examined. There are certain difficulties concerned with the standardization of fluorine spectra since line positions are very sensitive to the choice of solvent. The data in Table 5.5, which were determined by Evans, show this very clearly. The standardization procedure developed by Tiers (p. 48) appears to provide reliable shielding values.[31]

TABLE 5.4[29] THE MAGNETIC PROPERTIES OF SOME NUCLEI

Isotope	Natural abundance	Spin No. I	μ (nuclear magnetons)	Q quadrupole moment $e.10^{-24}$ cm^2
^{1}H	99·98	$\frac{1}{2}$	2·79255	
^{2}H	0·0156	1	0·85735	0·0027
^{3}H	0·0	$\frac{1}{2}$	2·9786	
^{12}C	98·9	0		
^{13}C	1·1	$\frac{1}{2}$	0·70225	
^{14}N	99·62	1	0·40365	0·02
^{15}N	0·38	$\frac{1}{2}$	0·2830	
^{16}O	99·757	0		
^{17}O	0·039	$\frac{5}{2}$	$-1\cdot8928$	$-0\cdot005$
^{18}O	0·204	0		
^{19}F	100	$\frac{1}{2}$	2·6285	
^{28}Si	92·28	0		
^{29}Si	4·67	$\frac{1}{2}$	$-0\cdot5549$	
^{30}Si	3·05	0		
^{31}P	100	$\frac{1}{2}$	1·1316	
^{32}S	95·06	0		
^{33}S	0·74	$\frac{3}{2}$	0·6429	$-0\cdot08$
^{34}S	0	0		
^{35}Cl	75·4	$\frac{3}{2}$	0·8219	$-0\cdot79$
^{37}Cl	24·6	$\frac{3}{2}$	0·6841	$-0\cdot062$
^{79}Br	50·5	$\frac{3}{2}$	2·1058	0·3
^{81}Br	49·5	$\frac{3}{2}$	2·2696	0·2
^{127}I	100	$\frac{5}{2}$	2·8086	$-0\cdot6$

The ϕ values (p. 48) of eleven organic fluorine compounds are listed in Table 5.6.[31] The values roughly confirm the theoretically predicted relation between the ionic character of the C—F bond and the chemical shift, made by Saika and Slichter.[28] This relation has been rigidly established by Taft for a number of *m* and *p*-substituted

TABLE 5.5 THE EFFECT OF SOLVENT ON THE FLUORINE
RESONANCE OF BENZOTRIFLUORIDE

Solvent	Shift (p.p.m.) at infinite dilution relative to $C_6H_5CF_3$ as external standard
Methylene iodide	−5·55*
Bromoform	−3·80
Carbon disulphide	−2·08
Carbon tetrachloride	−1·48
Methylene chloride	−1·20
Benzene	−1·08
Ethanol	0·055
n-Heptane	0·22
Ether	0·30
Perfluoroheptane	2·68

* Negative values denote a paramagnetic shift.

benzenes.[32] Measurements of the fluorine chemical shifts for quite a large number of organic fluorine compounds have been reported in the literature.[31–41] Although these values have not been obtained by Tiers' method, and are therefore subject to solvent effects of the order indicated in Table 5.5, the range of fluorine shifts is so

TABLE 5.6[31] FLUORINE CHEMICAL SHIFTS
IN SOME ORGANIC FLUORINE COMPOUNDS

Compound	ϕ (p.p.m.)
$C_6H_5SO_2F$	−65·50
$CFBr_3$	− 7·40
CF_2Br_2	− 6·77
$(BrCF_2)_2$	63·75
$C_6H_5CF_3$	67·75
CF_3CO_2H	76·54
CF_3CCl_3	82·20
C_6H_5F	113·12
$(CF_2CCl_2)_2$	176·24
$n\text{-}C_6H_{13}F$	219·02

large that useful correlations can still be made (e.g. ref. 38). We may also note that the fields associated with paramagnetic and interatomic diamagnetic circulations on neighbouring carbon atoms, which are important in the shielding of protons, will make only a minor contribution (0–4 p.p.m.) to fluorine shifts.

5.5 PHOSPHORUS (³¹P)

The resonance frequency of the phosphorus nucleus lies well below that of the proton at the same applied field and the signal strength of the phosphorus resonance is much less than that of either the hydrogen or fluorine resonance observed under equivalent conditions. However, the large range of the chemical shifts for phosphorus, coupled with the fact that most of the molecules studied contain only one or two phosphorus nuclei, permit the toleration of a lower order of resolution. Consequently, the signal-to-noise ratio can be increased by the use of large samples (p. 40).

The chemical shifts of the phorphorus nucleus are referred to 85 per cent aqueous phosphoric acid used as an external standard.* Volume susceptibility corrections may also be neglected. Line positions in various solvents may vary by $\pm 4 \cdot 0$ p.p.m.[42] and as yet no standard reference procedure has been evolved. Indeed, the need for working at high concentrations in a variety of different solvents makes the problem of developing a standard procedure a formidable one and the solvent shifts are not too serious in view of the range of observed phosphorus shifts (*ca.* 400 p.p.m.).

Several investigations of phosphorus chemical shifts have been reported[42–46] and the values have been interpreted in terms of the local paramagnetic effect of Saika and Slichter[28] suitably corrected for the hybridization of phosphorus in its various valence states.[42,47]

Although only comparatively few papers dealing with phosphorus magnetic resonance have appeared it is apparent that the method will be of great importance in the rapidly expanding field of organophosphorus chemistry. Chemical shifts and spin spin coupling constants both give information which is not readily available from other sources. There are three major compilations of chemical shift data[42,43,46] which cover the main classes of triply and quadruply connected phosphorus and polycondensed phosphorus derivatives. Van Wazer, Callis, Shoolery and Jones[44] have shown that substituents make an approximately constant contribution to the shielding of phosphorus in triply connected derivatives. These shielding constants are given in Table 5.7 and the line position of $R^1R^2R^3P$ relative to orthophosphoric acid is obtained by summing the appropriate values for R^1, R^2 and R^3. The accuracy of predicted values is ± 10–20 p.p.m. There is some evidence of additivity of substituent effects in quadruply connected phosphorus derivatives but the shifts in this series are best obtained from the correlation table of Finegold.[46]

II   III

An important feature of phosphorus magnetic resonance is the very large (500–700 c/s) spin–spin coupling constant (J_{PH}) between hydrogen and phosphorus

*The determination of line position is made directly from the oscilloscope display. The reference is first examined and its line position on the oscilloscope noted. The reference is then replaced by the sample and the signal of the latter is modulated at a frequency which causes one of the side bands to fall in the same position as that previously occupied by the reference signal. Because of the lower accuracy required for phosphorus shifts errors introduced by any variation in the applied field strength during the replacement operation are negligible.

which are directly bonded to each other.[45,46] This splitting provides a convenient means of distinguishing between the tautomers (II) and (III) (X = O,S). A consideration of chemical shifts and spin–spin coupling constants has led to the solution of several important problems in phosphorus chemistry.[45]

TABLE 5.7 SHIELDING CONSTANTS FOR
SUBSTITUENTS IN TRIPLY CONNECTED
PHOSPHORUS DERIVATIVES

Substituent*	Shielding constant
Br	−80
Cl	−74
I	−67
—PX$_2$	−60
OR	−56
NR$_2$	−47·5
OPh	−42·5
F	−27
S	−23
Ph	0
R	20
H	69

* R = alkyl.

5.6 CARBON (^{13}C)

A recent and exciting development in nuclear magnetic resonance spectroscopy has been the observation of absorption spectra of ^{13}C in organic molecules.[48,49] Although the natural abundance of ^{13}C is only 1·1 per cent it can nevertheless be studied with standard high resolution equipment. Lauterbur[48] has developed a technique, utilizing dispersion signals recorded with sweep rates of the order of 1000 cycles per minute, which enables the detection of signals from compounds with molecular weights up to 400. An important consequence of the low abundance is that the probability of a molecule containing two ^{13}C nuclei in close proximity to each other is very low. For this reason splitting due to spin–spin coupling between ^{13}C nuclei is not observed.

The chemical shifts of ^{13}C in various environments extend over 400 p.p.m., which is roughly comparable with the ranges observed for fluorine and phosphorus. Standardization of spectra can be done with an internal reference or by the replacement method used for phosphorus resonance (p. 77). Susceptibility corrections are insignificant and the magnitude of medium effects has not been established. Lauterbur[50] has chosen the line position of the carboxyl carbon nucleus in acetic acid as the arbitrary zero of reference.

Figure 5.6, which is a reproduction of the spectrum of dimethyl acetylenedicarboxylate,[50] gives an indication of the quality of ^{13}C spectra obtainable by Lauterbur's procedure. We may note the quartet structure of the methyl group band which arises from coupling of the ^{13}C nucleus with the three protons. The coupling between directly bonded ^{13}C and hydrogen is of the order of 120–200 c/s. Coupling constants of this type can also be determined from proton spectra.[51]

As a great many simple organic molecules are readily available, the ^{13}C nucleus is ideal for testing the Saika–Slichter theory for the shielding of nuclei other than hydrogen (p. 75). Lauterbur has established a number of linear relations between the chemical shift in ^{13}C—X and the electronegativity of X, which confirm the shielding theory.

From the organic chemist's point of view one of the most attractive features of ^{13}C spectroscopy is that it can provide direct information about carbon atoms which do not bear hydrogen atoms, such as in carbonyl groups. As yet only one attempt to apply the method to a structural problem has been reported.[52] A major improvement of the signal-to-noise ratio is required before the technique can be applied to complex structural problems for at the moment measurements are confined to molecules of low molecular weight which are liquids or which readily give highly concentrated solutions.

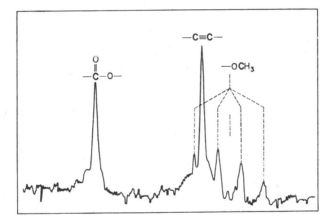

Fɪɢ. 5.6 ^{13}C magnetic resonance spectrum (8·5 Mc) of dimethyl acetylenedicarboxylate. (after Lauterbur[50])

Lauterbur[50] has drawn attention to the feasibility of using ^{13}C labelled intermediates in biogenetic studies. In many cases the labelling pattern in the products could be determined directly from their ^{13}C spectra. This would obviate the need for elaborate degradative procedures which are at present a feature of experiments employing the radioisotope ^{14}C as a label.

5.7 NITROGEN (^{14}N), OXYGEN (^{17}O) AND DEUTERIUM (^{2}H)

Chemical shifts have been observed for the nitrogen (^{14}N) nucleus in various molecular environments,[53,54,55,56,57] and a number of correlations with structure have been proposed.[57] Because the nitrogen nucleus possesses a quadrupole moment the observed signals are broad and presumably line widths may give some information about asymmetry of the electronic environments of nitrogen in different molecules.

Although chemical shifts have been observed for ^{17}O in some simple molecules[58,59] the natural abundance is too low to permit the routine study of this nucleus in organic compounds. Nuclear magnetic resonance spectroscopy of ^{17}O may possibly find applications in studies of reaction mechanisms.

As yet no observations of deuterium magnetic resonance in organic compounds have been reported although such experiments appear feasible. The direct examination of deuterium in compounds resulting from deuterium exchange reactions (e.g. the α-deuteration of ketones) might well yield results of structural significance and the interpretation of chemical shifts for deuterium could be based on the proton correlation tables. Deuterium has a small quadrupole moment so that some broadening of absorption lines may be anticipated.

REFERENCES

1. J. T. ARNOLD and M. E. PACKARD, *J. Chem. Phys.* **19**, 1608 (1951).
2. U. LIDDEL and N. F. RAMSAY, *ibid.*, 1608.
3. W. G. SCHNEIDER, H. J. BERNSTEIN and J. A. POPLE, *J. Chem. Phys.* **28**, 601 (1958); see also H. S. GUTOWSKY, *Ann. New York Acad Sci.* **70**, 786 (1958); A. A. BOTHNER-BY and C. NAARCOLIN, *J. Am. Chem. Soc.* **80**, 1728 (1958), footnote 17.
4. I. WEINBERG and J. R. ZIMMERMAN, *J. Chem. Phys.* **23**, 748 (1955).
5. C. M. HUGGINS, G. C. PIMENTEL and J. N. SHOOLERY, *ibid.*, 1244.
6. C. M. HUGGINS, G. C. PIMENTEL and J. N. SHOOLERY, *J. Phys. Chem.* **60**, 1311 (1956).
7. A. D. COHEN and C. REID,. *J. Chem. Phys.* **25**, 790 (1956).
8. E. D. BECKER, U. LIDDELL, and J. N. SHOOLERY, *J. Molecular Spectroscopy* **2**, 1 (1958).
9. K. TOYODA, T. IKENOUE, and T. ISOBE, *J. Chem. Phys.* **28**, 356 (1958).
10. L. W. REEVES and W. G. SCHNEIDER, *Trans. Faraday Soc.* **54**, 314 (1958).
11. M. SAUNDERS AND J. B. HYNE, *J. Chem. Phys.* **29**, 253 (1958).
12. J. GRÄNATHER, *Helv. Phys. Acta.* **31**, 734 (1958).
12A. L. W. REEVES and W. G. SCHNEIDER, *Canad. J. Chem.* **35**, 251 (1957); A. A. BOTHNER-BY and R. E. GLICK, *J. Chem. Phys.* **26**, 1651 (1957).
13. N. F. CHAMBERLAIN, *Anal. Chem.* **31**, 56 (1959).
14. H. S. JARRET, M. S. SADLER and J. N. SHOOLERY, *J. Chem. Phys.* **21**, 2092 (1953).
15. B. N. BHAR, *Arkiv Kemi* **10**, 223 (1956); B. N. BHAR and G. LINDSTRÖM, *J. Chem. Phys.* **23**, 1958 (1955); B. N. BHAR, W. FORSLING, and G. LINDSTRÖM, *Arkiv. Fys.* **10**, 59 (1956).
16. L. W. REEVES, *Can. J. Chem.* **35**, 1351 (1957).
17. W. G. SCHNEIDER and L. W. REEVES, *Ann. New York Acad. Sci.* **70**, 858 (1958).
18. J. D. ROBERTS, *J. Am. Chem. Soc.* **78**, 4495 (1956).
19. R. A. OGG, *J. Chem. Phys.* **22**, 560 (1954).
20. *Idem., Discuss. Faraday Soc.* **17**, 215 (1954).
21. E. GRUNWALD, A. LOEWENSTEIN, and S. MEIBOOM, *J. Chem. Phys.* **27**, 630 (1957).
22. G. V. D. TIERS and F. A. BOVEY, *J. Phys. Chem.* **63**, 302 (1959).
23. A. BERGER, A. LOEWENSTEIN, and S. MEIBOOM, *J. Am. Chem. Soc.* **81**, 62 (1959).
24. "N.M.R. at Work", No. 50. Issued by Varian Associates Ltd.
25. L. H. MEYER, A. SAIKA, and H. S. GUTOWSKY, *J. Am. Chem. Soc.* **75**, 4567 (1953).
26. R. J. ABRAHAM, J. A. POPLE, and H. J. BERNSTEIN, *Canad. J. Chem.* **36**, 1302 (1958).
27. F. A. COTTON, J. L. DOWN, and G. WILKINSON, *J. Chem. Soc.* 833 (1959) and references given therein.
28. A. SAIKA and C. P. SLICHTER, *J. Chem. Phys.* **22**, 26 (1954).
29. N. F. RAMSEY, *Nuclear Moments*, Wiley, New York, 1953.
30. D. F. EVANS, *Proc. Chem. Soc.* 115 (1958); cf. R. E. GLICK and S. J. EHRENSON, *J. Phys. Chem.* **62**, 1599 (1958).
31. G. FILIPOVICH and G. V. D. TIERS, *J. Phys. Chem.* **63**, 761 (1959).
32. R. W. TAFT, *J. Am. Chem. Soc.* **79**, 1045 (1957).
33. H. S. GUTOWSKY, D. W. McCALL, B. R. McGEAVEY, and L. H. MEYER, *J. Am. Chem. Soc.* **74**, 4809 (1952).
34. L. H. MEYER and H. S. GUTOWSKY, *J. Phys. Chem.* **57**, 481 (1953).
35. G. V. D. TIERS, *J. Am. Chem. Soc.* **78**, 2914 (1956).
36. W. D. PHILLIPS, *J. Chem. Phys.* **25**, 949 (1956).
37. J. J. DRYSDALE and W. D. PHILLIPS, *J. Am. Chem. Soc.* **79**, 319 (1957).
38. N. MULLER, P. C. LAUTERBUR, and G. F. SVATOS, *ibid.*, 1043, 1807.
39. G. V. D. TIERS, *ibid.*, 5585.

40. E. Schnell and E. G. Rochow, *J. Inorg. Nucl. Chem.* **6**, 303 (1958).
41. R. E. Richards and T. Schaeffer, *Trans. Faraday Soc.* **54**, 1449 (1958).
42. N. Muller, P. C. Lauterbur, and J. Goldenson, *J. Am. Chem. Soc.* **78**, 3557 (1956).
43. J. R. Van Wazer, C. F. Callis, and J. N. Shoolery, *J. Am. Chem. Soc.* **77**, 4945 (1955).
44. J. R. Van Wazer, C. F. Callis, J. N. Shoolery, and R. C. Jones, *ibid.* **78**, 5715 (1956).
45. C. F. Callis, J. R. Van Wazer, J. N. Shoolery, and W. A. Anderson, *ibid.* **79**, 2719 (1957).
46. H. Finegold, *Ann. New York Acad. Sci.* **70**, 875 (1958).
47. J. R. Parks, *J. Am. Chem. Soc.* **79**, 757 (1957).
48. P. C. Lauterbur, *J. Chem. Phys.* **26**, 217 (1957).
49. C. H. Holm, *ibid.*, 707.
50. P. C. Lauterbur, *Ann. New York Acad. Sci.* **70**, 841 (1958).
51. A. D. Cohen, N. Sheppard, and J. J. Turner, *Proc. Chem. Soc.* 118 (1958).
52. F. A. Cotton, D. Danti, J. S. Waugh, and R. W. Fessenden, *J. Chem. Phys.* **29**, 1427 (1958).
53. W. G. Procter and F. C. Yu, *Phys. Rev.* **77**, 717 (1950).
54 Y. Masuda and T. Kanda, *J. Phys. Soc. Japan* **8**, 432 (1953).
55. B. E. Holder and M. P. Klein, *J. Chem. Phys.* **23**, 1956 (1955).
56. R. A. Ogg and J. D. Ray, *ibid.* **26**, 1339 (1957).
57. B. M. Schmidt, L. Carlton Brown, and D. Williams, *J. Molecular Spectroscopy* **2**, 539, 551 (1958); **3**, 30 (1959).
58. F. Alder and F. C. Yu, *Phys. Rev.* **81**, 1067 (1951).
59. H. E. Weaver, B. M. Tolbert, and R. C. La Force, *J. Chem. Phys.* **23**, 1956 (1955).

CHAPTER 6

THE INTERPRETATION OF THE SPECTRA OF COMPLEX ORGANIC MOLECULES

6.1 INTRODUCTION

THE EXACT manner in which nuclear resonance spectroscopy may be used to elucidate the structure of an organic molecule will vary from case to case. Since it is rarely possible to derive a structure solely from a nuclear magnetic resonance spectrum and an empirical formula, we have in general to consider the former in conjunction with chemical evidence and other spectroscopic data. In this present chapter we shall therefore outline some of the more important factors which enter into the interpretation of spectra, and provide examples which it is hoped will illustrate some of the ways in which structural information can be obtained.

The present generation of organic chemists makes considerable use of ultra-violet and infrared spectroscopy in structure determination, and we will thus find it instructive to contrast these techniques with that of nuclear magnetic resonance spectroscopy. The ultraviolet and visible spectrum usually provides information about just one or two structural features of a complex molecule. This limitation is of some advantage since the spectra contain only a few absorption bands the character of which may be largely uninfluenced by the rest of the molecule. On the other hand every part of a complex molecule contributes to its infrared spectrum, which as a result is so complicated that the organic chemist finds only relatively few bands provide structural information. The role of nuclear magnetic resonance spectroscopy in structural organic chemistry lies between the other two methods. Many more structural features give rise to distinctive nuclear magnetic resonance absorption than to ultraviolet or visible absorption, and yet the nuclear spectrum is as a rule far less complex than corresponding infrared spectrum, so that for even quite complex molecules we may hope to assign every band in the spectrum. The approach for all three methods is essentially empirical, and we shall rely heavily on the correlation tables in Chapters 4 and 5. This means that the organic chemist will have a new set of "useful" numbers to learn, and there is no doubt that within a year or so he will be as familiar with the τ-values of various types of methyl groups etc. as he is at present with carbonyl stretching frequencies or with absorption maxima in the electronic spectra of polyenes. The three spectroscopic methods frequently give complementary information, and there is no question of nuclear magnetic resonance spectroscopy superseding the other two. There is, however, one feature of nuclear magnetic resonance spectroscopy which is likely to give it an advantage over other methods. This concerns the possibility of developing semi-empirical methods for the prediction of proton line positions, which will be applicable to complex molecules. Such methods are at present in their infancy but it is hoped that the subject matter of Chapter 7 will indicate their potential and inspire the research necessary to bring them to maturity.

When we examine a nuclear magnetic resonance spectrum with a view to making assignments we are guided by three considerations, namely line positions, intensities, and spin–spin multiplicities. The first problem in interpretation involves the distinction between signals which correspond to transitions of nuclei which are not spin–spin coupled to other nuclei, and those signals which are components of spin–spin multiplets. In order to do this we need to consider spin–spin coupling in greater detail than attempted in Chapter 2.

6.2 ELECTRON COUPLED SPIN–SPIN INTERACTIONS

There are various ways in which we may proceed to determine whether a group of lines in a spectrum arise from non-equivalent (p. 19) nuclei or whether they constitute spin–spin multiplets, and the approach chosen will depend largely on the nature of the problem. A common situation is that in which the structure of a compound has been reduced to several closely related possibilities. It is then possible to predict the expected multiplicity of a given band for each of the conceivable structures, so that provided the appropriate signals can be identified in the spectrum a precise structure can be determined. An example of this procedure is provided by the investigation of the cycloheptatrienecarboxylic acids carried out by Doering and his collaborators.[1] Four chemically distinct cycloheptatrienecarboxylic acids are known and are clearly the different positional isomers (I)–(VI).

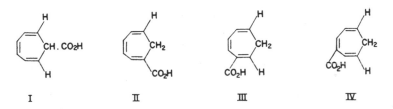

I   II   III   IV

The corresponding esters contain three classes of protons, namely olefinic, methoxylic, and aliphatic, which give rise to absorption in different parts of the proton spectrum (see Chapter 4). The appearance of the aliphatic band can be predicted for each isomer. Thus for (I), (III) and (IV) a triplet is expected (p. 23) because in each of these molecules the aliphatic proton or protons are flanked by *two* olefinic protons to each of which it should be equally (approximately) coupled. In contrast (II) should give rise to a doublet in the aliphatic region since there is only *one* olefinic proton adjacent to the methylene group. In fact only one of the four esters gave an aliphatic doublet. The remaining three isomers gave triplets in the aliphatic region and of these one could be assigned the structure (I) from a consideration of relative intensities.

As a further example we may note that the correct interpretation of the spectrum of mesityl oxide (Fig. 6.1) is made possible by the observation that the highest frequency band is a doublet. At first sight it is tempting to assign the middle band (relative intensity, 6) to the two methyl groups of the isopropylidene residue. However the doublet at higher frequency cannot be due to the CH_3CO protons since these could not couple with the olefinic proton to give splittings of the observed order. Thus the two allylic methyl groups must absorb at different frequencies and one band must overlap with the CH_3CO line.[2]

When little is known about the structure of a compound the problem is more difficult since *a priori* predictions of multiplicity are no longer possible. Nevertheless, spin–spin multiplets can frequently be recognized as such. One of the most powerful techniques for distinguishing chemical shifts from spin–spin couplings involves the determination of the spectrum at two different field strengths, for as we have seen the spin–spin coupling constant, *J*, is unaltered by changes in field strength whereas the chemical shifts are directly proportional to such changes. Thus, if the separation (in cycles per second) of a group of lines is the same in spectra determined at, say, 40 and 60 Mc, the lines must constitute a spin–spin multiplet. This test is not available to all investigators since it cannot be made with instruments employing permanent magnets and even with electromagnetic

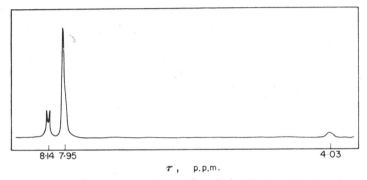

FIG. 6.1   The proton spectrum of mesityl oxide in CCl₄. (40 Mc).

spectrometers it requires additional equipment. Furthermore, as we shall presently, the appearance of a spin–spin multiplet is not always independent of field strength even though the coupling constants are invariant. For these reasons it is important to be able to recognize characteristic patterns and separations of lines arising from spin–spin multiplicity.

The spin–spin coupling constants for protons have values which are to some extent characteristic of their structural and stereochemical relationships and some of the more useful values are listed in Table 6.1. Values of proton–fluorine and fluorine–fluorine coupling constants are given in Table 6.2.

Theoretical studies of the magnitudes of coupling constants have yielded some interesting results. Of particular significance are the calculations by Karplus[6] of J_{ab} for the various conformations of the system (V). These calculations relate the magnitude of the coupling constant, J_{ab}, to the dihedral angle, ϕ, between the planes $H_a C_1 C_2$ and $H_b C_2 C_1$ and there is some experimental confirmation of the results (Table 6.3). Thus studies of pyranose monosaccharides [e.g. (VI), (VII) and (VIII)] have shown that the coupling constants between vicinal hydrogen atoms in diaxial ($\phi = 180°$), diequatorial ($\phi = 60°$) and axial equatorial ($\phi = 60°$) conformations are *ca.* 7, 3 and 3 c/s respectively.[7] Unfortunately, there are other examples which are at variance with the theoretical results. For instance, the *cis* ($\phi = 0°$) and *trans* ($\phi = 120°$) coupling constants in β-propiolactone (IX)[8], *trans-* dibromocyclopropane (X)[9] and 2:3-dihydrofuran (Fig. 6.2)[9] are nearly equal.

TABLE 6.1 PROTON SPIN–SPIN COUPLING CONSTANTS*

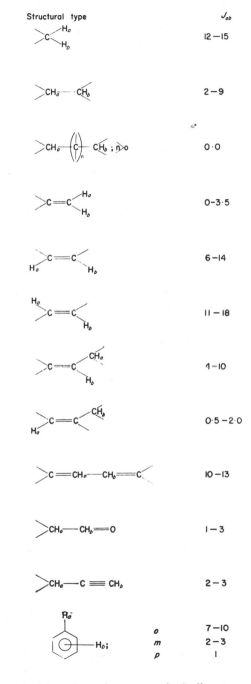

Structural type		J_{ab}
		12–15
		2–9
		0·0
		0–3·5
		6–14
		11–18
		4–10
		0·5–2·0
		10–13
		1–3
		2–3
	o	7–10
	m	2–3
	p	1

*These values are taken from the various sources in the literature and from the author's own work.

Anomalous splittings have been observed in cyclobutane derivatives,[10] and the coupling between the two classes of protons in cyclobutene is zero.[9]

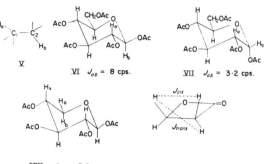

Coupling constants between alkyl protons in acyclic systems have values which are weighted means of all possible conformations. Two useful values are the

TABLE 6.2[3] PROTON FLUORINE AND FLUORINE–FLUORINE SPIN–SPIN
COUPLING CONSTANTS (c/s)

Structural type		J_{HF} (X=H)	J_{FF} (X=F)
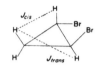		44 −81	158
⟩CX—CF⟨		7 −13[o,b]	
⟩CX—C—CF⟨		0	11[o]
⟩C=C⟨ (X) (F)		1 −8	33 − 58
(X)⟩C=C⟨ (F)		12 − 40	115 −124
⟨F⟩—X ;	o	6 −10	20
	m	6 − 5	2 − 4
	p	2	12 −15

o ref 4; *b* ref 5

TABLE 6.3. THE ANGULAR DEPENDENCE OF PROTON
SPIN–SPIN COUPLING CONSTANTS (SEE TEXT)

$\phi°$	J_{ab} (theor.)	J_{ab} (exp.)
0	8·2	
30	6·0	
60	1·7	2–4
90	−0·28	
120	2·2	
150	6·9	
180	9·2	5–8

coupling constants in ethyl groups, 6·7–7·2 c/s, and isopropyl groups, 5·7–6·8 c/s.

Proton coupling constants across double bonds also show a dependence on stereochemistry (Table 6.1). The calculated values[6] are somewhat lower than found in practice but they account well for the ratio, $J_{cis}/J_{trans} \sim 0·5$. The coupling constants for simple acyclic olefins usually lie well within the ranges given in Table 6.1 and are very useful for establishing the configurations of 1 : 2-disubstituted ethylenes. For example the stereochemistry (see XI) of the less stable of the two known isomers of β-methylmuconic acid follows from the observation that the two protons of the disubstituted double bond give rise to doublets with J =16 c/s. This value is almost equal to the coupling (J — 15·5 c/s) observed for the more stable isomer which is presumed to be *trans-trans*.[11]

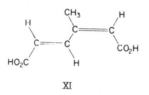

XI

The spin–spin coupling constants for olefinic protons in certain cyclic systems do not agree well with the values found for acyclic *cis*-olefins. The olefinic coupling constant in 2 : 3-dihydropyran is only 6·0 c/s. A more striking example is 2 : 3-dihydrofuran and, as several of the coupling constants in this molecule are anomalous, we shall discuss its spectrum in detail. The spectrum exhibits four bands, a consideration of the intensities and τ-values of which leads to the assignments shown in Fig. 6.2. There can be little doubt that these assignments are correct. The two bands arising from the olefinic protons are identical quartets the spacings of which correspond to $J = 3·1$ c/s. To account for these observations we have to postulate a rather remarkable set of coincidences, namely $J_{ab} = J_{ac} = J_{bc} = 3·1$ c/s. J_{ab}, the olefinic coupling constant and J_{bc} are thus substantially lower than any previously reported values, whereas the allylic coupling constant J_{ac} is much larger than usual (Table 6.1). To make matters worse the coupling between the two methylene groups is 9·1 c/s, the largest reported for an interaction of this type. The lines of the triplet of the "d" methylene group are rather broad. This may be due to a second order splitting (p. 24) or possibly it reflects a slight non-equivalence of the *cis* and *trans* coupling constants between the two methylene groups. The lines of "c" group are additionally broadened by coupling with the olefinic protons.

The foregoing discussion suggests that the values of coupling constants can play a useful role in structure determination but until we have a more satisfactory theory of spin–spin interaction we must exercise considerable caution when we compare data for various systems. *A structural proof based on the values of coupling constants will only be valid if data for very closely related model compounds are available.*

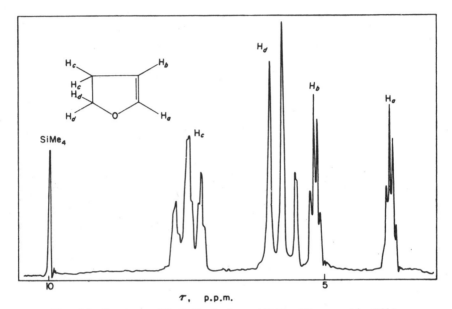

FIG. 6.2   Spectrum of 1 : 2-dihydrofuran (40 Mc; 10 per cent in CCl₄).

The recognition of characteristic intensity patterns can often permit the identification of a spin–spin multiplet in a complex spectrum. We have seen for proton-proton interactions that a doublet ideally should have an intensity ratio of 1 : 1, a triplet 1 : 2 : 1, a quartet 1 : 3 : 3 : 1, etc. (p. 23). If in a complex spectrum we observe a group of equally spaced lines which exhibits one of these typical intensity ratios we are immediately led to suspect spin–spin multiplicity. It is most important, particularly in proton spectroscopy, to realize that *simple integral intensity ratios represent an extreme situation and are only observed if the frequency difference between the two interacting groups of nuclei is large compared with the spin-spin coupling constant.* When a system departs from this limiting condition we may observe not only an alteration of the intensity ratios but also, in certain cases, *the appearance of additional lines in the multiplets.* Indeed many systems of nuclei for which the chemical shifts and coupling constants are of the same order give rise to multiplets which are completely unrecognizable in terms of the patterns predicted by the simple splitting rules (p. 23). Since bands of this type are quite frequently observed in the spectra of organic molecules we shall consider the more common situations in detail. In keeping with our present treatment of nuclear magnetic resonance as a whole we will confine ourselves to qualitative descriptions but it must be emphasized that in many cases accurate values of τ and J are only available from a mathematical analysis of the spectral data. Nevertheless if we can but recognize the appearance of complex patterns we will be in a stronger position to interpret the spectra of organic molecules.

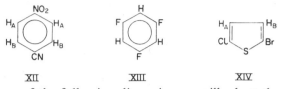

XII   XIII   XIV

For the purpose of the following discussion we will adopt the conventions and symbols introduced by Bernstein, Pople, and Schneider.[12] Groups of equivalent nuclei* for which the chemical shifts and coupling constants are of the same order, are symbolized by A_n, B_m, ... where the subscripts refer to the number of nuclei in the group and A, B, etc., are in order of increasing τ. Thus the four hydrogen atoms in *p*-nitrobenzonitrile (XII) constitute an A_2B_2 system. If the groups of nuclei, A, B, ..., are coupled to other nuclei, the chemical shifts of which are very different from A, B, ..., the latter are symbolized by X_n, Y_m, ... For example, symmetrical trifluorobenzene (XIII) is termed an A_3X_3 system. If there is only one nucleus in a group the subscript is usually omitted, as in A_2B, AB_2X_2, etc. We shall only consider examples in which all nuclei have $I = \frac{1}{2}$.

THE AB SYSTEM

The simplest system of interacting nuclei is the two spin system, AB, which is exemplified by the protons of 2-bromo-4-chlorothiophene (XIV). The two extreme cases of the AB system are AX and a pair of equivalent nuclei, A_2. The AX system gives rise to a pair of doublets the lines of which are of equal intensity in accordance with the simple splitting rules (p. 23). A pair of equivalent nuclei give rise to a single absorption line (p. 23). The intermediate situation in which the chemical shift, $(\delta_B - \delta_A)$ between the two nuclei is comparable to J_{AB} also consists of a pair of doublets but the intensities of the four lines are no longer equal (Fig. 6.3). There is, in fact, a gradual transition from the AX to the A_2 system in which the intensities of the inner pair of lines of the four line spectrum increase at the expense of the outer pair. In the AX spectrum the centre of gravity of the A band i.e. position from which we compute the τ-value of A, is the mid-point of the A doublet. As $J_{AB}/(\delta_B - \delta_A)$ increases the centre of gravity of each band moves towards its inner component. If we are to measure accurate τ-values in AB systems we have to know the centre of gravity corresponding to each value of $J_{AB}/(\delta_B - \delta_A)$. Simple expressions for centres of gravity and also the intensity ratios in terms of J_{AB} and δ are available. If we label the lines of the spectrum *1*, *2*, *3*, and *4* in order of increasing shielding (i.e. decreasing separation from the line of tetramethylsilane) and call the mid-point of the spectrum O (Fig. 6.3), the following relations in which the positions of *1*, *2*, *3*, and *4* are expressed in c/s, can be derived.[13,12]

$$(3-4) = (1-2) = J_{AB} \tag{1}$$

$$(1-3) = (2-4) = \sqrt{(\delta_B - \delta_A)^2 + J_{AB}^2} \tag{2}$$

*i.e., each group comprises of nuclei with the same chemical shift.

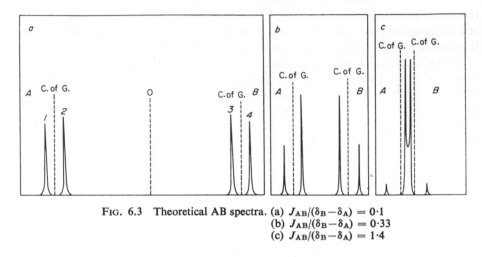

FIG. 6.3   Theoretical AB spectra. (a) $J_{AB}/(\delta_B - \delta_A) = 0 \cdot 1$
(b) $J_{AB}/(\delta_B - \delta_A) = 0 \cdot 33$
(c) $J_{AB}/(\delta_B - \delta_A) = 1 \cdot 4$

Equation (2) allows the determination of $(\delta_B - \delta_A)$ and the actual values of δ_A and δ_B are then found by adding and subtracting $\frac{1}{2}(\delta_B - \delta_A)$ to and from O, respectively. The relative intensities are given by (3) and (4).

$$1 = 4 = 1 - J_{AB}[(\delta_B - \delta_A)^2 + J_{AB}^2]^{-\frac{1}{2}} \qquad (3)$$

$$2 = 3 = 1 + J_{AB}[(\delta_B - \delta_A)^2 + J_{AB}^2]^{-\frac{1}{2}} \qquad (4)$$

The error introduced by taking the mid-points of the doublets for δ_A and δ_B if $J_{AB}/(\delta_B - \delta_A)$ is equal to $\frac{1}{3}$, and $J_{AB} = 10$ c/s is only 0·5 c/s even though the intensity ratio of the doublet components is 2 : 1.

ABX_n SYSTEMS

The spectrum of the simple AB system is modified if one or both nuclei are coupled to a third nucleus X. Intuitively we might expect a twelve line spectrum to result, since each of the original four AB lines should be split into doublets and the X line should appear as a quartet. In fact, the ABX system frequently does consist of twelve lines.* However, an extension of this argument suggests that if either J_{AX} or J_{BX} is zero the spectrum should degenerate to ten lines. In fact, the spectra of systems in which J_{AX} or J_{BX} is zero still exhibit twelve lines and we must conclude that simple intuitive reasoning cannot lead to the successful prediction of the multiplicities of the more complicated spin systems.

Figure 6.4 shows a hypothetical ABX spectrum in relation to that of the system in which X is not coupled to either A or B (i.e. $J_{AX} = J_{BX} = 0$). The coupling constant J_{AB} can be evaluated directly from the ABX spectrum since it is equal to the separations of lines *1* and *3*, *2* and *4*, *5* and *7*, and *6* and *8*. The separations (*1*, *2*) and (*3*, *4*) are *not* equal J_{AX} but are a function of all coupling constants and the chemical shift $\delta_{AB}(= \delta_B - \delta_A)$. Explicit expressions for the frequencies and intensities of lines in the ABX spectrum have been derived[12] and

---

*In theory ABX spectra can have fourteen lines. Two of these are combination transitions corresponding to the simultaneous excitation of two nuclei and are usually too weak to be observed.

these can be used to evaluate δ_{AB}, J_{AX} and J_{BX}. In general, the values of these last three parameters are not uniquely determined unless accurate intensities for the lines in the spectrum are available.

If the coupling constants J_{AX} and J_{BX} are equal the spectrum is simplified to one of eleven lines in which the splittings (*1, 2*), (*3, 4*), (*5, 6*), and (*7, 8*) are all equal and lines *10* and *11* are coincident. Certain combinations of values for the various parameters can reduce the X band to a doublet making the splittings (*1, 2*) and (*3, 4*) or (*5, 6*) and (*7, 8*) vanish. We shall meet this situation in the example discussed on p. 108. If the splittings (*1, 2*), (*3, 4*), etc. are large the A and B bands may overlap (cf. Fig. 6.4).

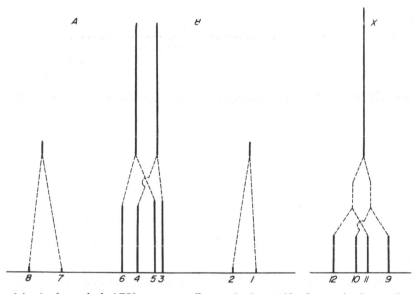

FIG. 6.4   A theoretical ABX spectrum ($\delta_{AB} = 5$; $J_{AB} = 10$; $J_{AX} = 4$; $J_{BX} = 2$) and its relation to the AB and X spectra.

Analyses of the ABX$_3$ systems has been reported,[13a] the spectra of such systems may contain lines. Their general appearance can sometimes be recognized in terms of the AB, AX, and BX patterns as, for instance, in the spectrum of methyl *trans*-crotonate (Fig. 6.5).

ABC AND AB$_2$ SYSTEMS

The spectrum of the ABX system exhibits certain features of symmetry. For instance the X band is a symmetrical quartet and some of the separations in the A and B bands are equal [e.g. (*1, 2*) = (*3, 4*) and (*5, 6*) = (*7, 8*)]. These features are absent in the spectra of ABC systems (Fig. 6.6). Furthermore, it is no longer possible to derive explicit expressions for frequencies and intensities. Analysis of the ABC problem[12] involves the solution of two third order secular determinants so that calculation of shifts and coupling constants requires a tedious trial and error procedure which is best carried out with an electronic computor. It is to be hoped that eventually the requisite data for various combinations of values of

J_{AB}, J_{AC}, J_{BC}, δ_{AB} and δ_{AC} will be calculated and tabulated. Some ABC systems approximate to ABX and can be quite satisfactorily analysed as such.[14]

A special case of ABC, namely AB_2 is encountered quite frequently in organic molecules. These systems give rise to a spectrum of nine lines, one of which is a weak combination transition (see footnote to p. 90). The analysis of AB_2 spectra is straightforward. The relative line separations and intensities are determined solely by J_{AB}/δ_{AB} and Bernstein, Pople and Schneider[12] have derived explicit expressions for this purpose. They have also tabulated relative line positions for various values of J_{AB}/δ_{AB}. Richards and Schaefer[14] have examined a number of spectra of AB_2 (and A_2B). These are reproduced in Fig. 6.7 and are an excellent guide to the general appearance of the spectrum for various values of J_{AB}/δ_{AB}. The centre of gravity of the A band coincides with line 3 and that of B with the mean of lines 5 and 7. Richards and Schaefer[14] have drawn attention to the fact that the coupling between A and each of the B nuclei may not be equal. This does not alter the nature of the spectrum but the calculated value of "J_{AB}" now refers to the average of the two AB coupling constants. The molecules in Figs. 6.7A and c are believed to have unequal AB coupling constants.

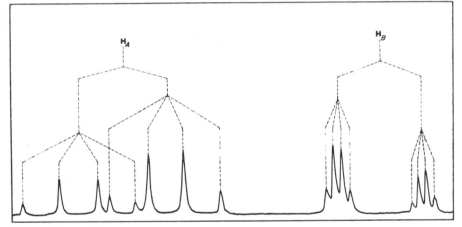

FIG. 6.5. An ABX_3 spectrum. The spectrum of the olefinic protons of methyl *trans*-crotonate (40 Mc/s.; 10% CCl_4).

A_2X_2 AND A_2B_2 SYSTEMS

The spectra of the A_2X_2 and A_2B_2 systems consist of two bands each containing a maximum of ten and twelve lines, respectively. Both spectra are characterized by symmetry about the mid-point of the spectrum so that the band of the A group is the mirror image of that of the B or X group. The A_2X_2 spectrum has the additional feature that the A and X bands are themselves symmetrical.

We shall consider the A_2X_2 system first and because of the symmetry of the spectrum as a whole we need only discuss one of the bands (A or X). There are four coupling constants, viz. J_{AA}, J_{XX}, J_{AX} and J'_{AX} (Fig. 6.8), which determine the separation and intensities of the components of each band so that for the first time we encounter a system in which coupling between equivalent atoms plays a part in determining the nature of the spectrum. Explicit expressions for separations and

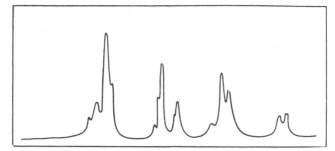

FIG. 6.6 An ABC spectrum. The proton spectrum of 2 : 4-dinitrochlorobenzene at 29·9 Mc.
(after R. E. Richards adn T. Schaefer[14]).

intensities have been derived by McConnell, McLean and Reilly[15] so that the values of the four coupling constants can be computed.*

The simplest system is that in which J_{AX} and J'_{AX} are equal. In this case the spectrum is correctly predicted by the simple splitting rules (p. 23). Thus the spectrum of *trans*-dibromocyclopropane (X) (p. 86) consists of two triplets so that we can infer that $J_{cis} = J_{trans}$. Spectra of this type are independent of J_{AA} and J_{XX} and the spacing of the triplets gives J_{AX} directly.

A theoretical spectrum of an A_2X_2 system with J_{AX} not equal to J'_{AX} is shown in Fig. 6.9D. This pattern becomes somewhat simpler if one or more of the coupling

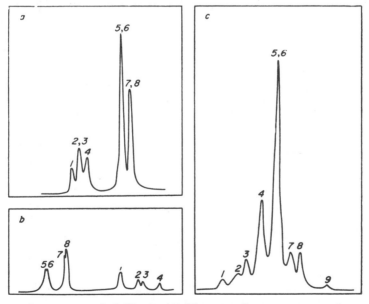

FIG. 6.7 Typical AB₂ spectra. The aromatic proton spectra of:
(a) 2 : 5-dichloronitrobenzene ($J/\delta_{AB} = 0·17$)
(b) 3-nitrosalicylic acid ($J/\delta_{AB} = 0·25$)
(c) 3-nitro-o-xylene ($J/\delta_{AB} = 0·77$)
(After R. E. Richards and T. Schaefer[14])

*Apart from J_{AX} and J'_{AX} the relative signs of the coupling constants are not determined.

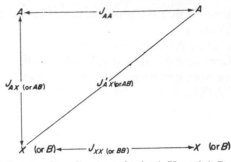

FIG. 6.8   Coupling Constants in the A_2X_2 and A_2B_2 system.

constants vanishes. Thus if J_{AA} or J_{XX} is equal to zero each band contains only six lines (Fig. 6.9c). If $J_{AA} = J_{XX}$ there will be eight lines in each band (Fig. 6.9B). The patterns indicated in Fig. 6.9 would all be radically altered by changing the values of the various coupling constants so that they cannot be regarded as "typical" of A_2X_2 systems. The only common feature of A_2X_2 spectra is the symmetrical nature of the bands.

As we progress from the A_2X_2 to the A_2B_2 system the spectrum becomes more complex since each band loses its symmetry and new lines develop. The patterns of the bands now depend on δ_{AB} as well as the four coupling constants. Explicit expressions are available for the intensities and positions of eight of the twelve possible lines in each band.[12,16] The remaining four require the solution of a fourth

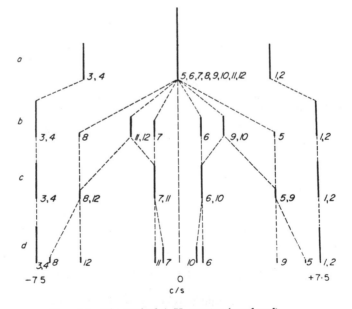

FIG. 6.9   Theoretical A_2X_2 spectra (one band)
(a) $J_{AX} = J'_{AX} = 5$ cps.
(b) $J_{AX} = 10;\ J'_{AX} = 5;\ J_{AA} = J_{XX} = 2$
(c) $J_{AX} = 10;\ J'_{AX} = 5;\ J_{AA} = 4;\ J_{XX} = 0$
(d) $J_{AX} = 10;\ J'_{AX} = 5;\ J_{AA} = 4;\ J_{XX} = 2$

order secular determinant so that the problem is similar to that discussed in connection with the ABC system.

In the A_2B_2 system as in A_2X_2 an equality of J_{AB} and J'_{AB} leads to a simpler spectrum which is independent of J_{AA} and J_{BB}. The relative positions of the seven lines in each band have been computed for a range of values of J_{AB}/δ_{AB}.[12]

Some examples of A_2X_2 and A_2B_2 spectra are shown in Fig. 6.10.

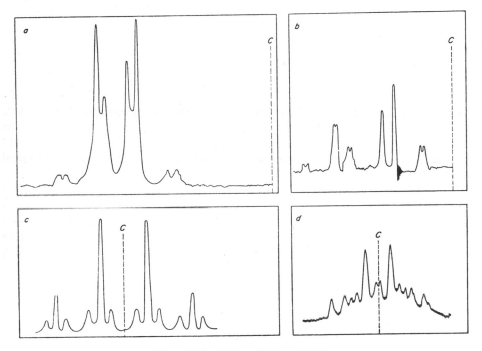

FIG. 6.10 A_2X_2 and A_2B_2 spectra.

   a. *cis-cis*-Dimethyl muconate (40 Mc). This spectrum is approximately an A_2X_2 type. Only the A band is shown. The complete spectrum is symmetrical about C.

   b. *trans-trans*-Dimethyl muconate (40 Mc). An A_2B_2 type. Only the A band is shown. The complete spectrum is symmetrical about C.

   c. *p*-Chloroiodobenzene (29·92 Mc). An A_2B_2 spectrum in which $J_{AA} = J_{BB}$ and $J'_{AB} = 0$ (after R. E. Richards and T. P. Schaefer[16]).

   d. Naphthalene (40 Mc). An A_2B_2 spectrum in which $J'_{AB} = 0$ (*cf.* ref. 12).

AB_3 SYSTEM

The fine structure of an AB_3 spectrum is determined by the chemical shift and the three AB coupling constants. The organic chemist quite frequently encounters the AB_3 in the form of the grouping CH_3—$\overset{/}{\underset{\backslash}{C}}H$. As the methyl group is invariably rotating rapidly about its threefold axis of symmetry the three AB coupling constants have the same average value so that we need only consider the case in which all the J_{AB}'s are equal.

The AB_3 system with only one J_{AB} has sixteen allowed transitions, two of which are combinations and therefore very weak.[17] Of the fourteen lines, eight arise from transitions of the B nuclei. If J_{AB} is of the order of 5–7 c/s it will not, in general, be possible to resolve all of these lines and a band envelope rather than a discrete line spectrum will often be observed. We shall concentrate our attention on the B group and describe the appearance of its absorption band as J_{AB}/δ_{AB} is increased. In an AX_3 system the X_3 band consists of a pair of sharp lines of equal intensity. In the region of $J_{AB}/\delta_{AB} = 0\cdot1$ the low frequency component is intensified at the expense of its partner and both lines are broadened. This trend is maintained until the high frequency components merely constitute an inflexion on the side of the band. At this stage the A and B bands will overlap so that the low frequency side of the B band will also be distorted. These band shapes are illustrated in Fig. 6.11. High values of J_{AB}/δ_{AB} are most frequently observed when the methyl group is attached to a saturated hydrocarbon fragment as in (XV). If (XV) is part

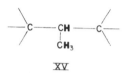

XV

of an acyclic system the value of the ratio J_{AB}/δ_{AB} leads to a spectrum of the type shown in Fig. 6.11B. In some cyclic systems such as *cis*-dimethylcyclohexane the shielding of the A-proton is greater than in the acyclic case and δ_{AB} correspondingly smaller so that the spectrum may be of the type 6.11C. It is important to realize that the ratio J_{AB}/δ_{AB} is inversely proportional to field strength so that a band of this type will have quite a different shape determined at 60 Mc than at 30 Mc.

The A_2B_3 System

No complete analysis of the A_2B_3 system has been reported. We shall encounter this system as ethyl groups in certain molecules. By analogy with the AB_3 system we expect many-line spectra which will lead to the observation of band envelopes. Accordingly we can best approach this problem by examining some actual spectra. The 40 Mc spectrum of diethyl ether (Fig. 6.12A) at moderate resolution approximates to an A_2X_2 system although at really high resolution additional fine structure is visible (cf. p. 24). As the chemical shift, δ_{AB} of the methylene and methyl groups decreases the components of the quartet and triplet broaden and the symmetry of each multiplet is lost. This trend is shown in Figs. 6.12B and C. If δ_{AB} is of the order of 10–20 c/s the A and B bands overlap and a band envelope of the type illustrated in 6.12D is observed.

Other spin systems which have been analysed include AB_2X_2,[18] A_2B_2X,[19] and A_6X_2 (for certain values of the coupling constants).[20] In principle, any spectrum can be calculated for a given set of parameters and the general procedure has been outlined.[12,15,21] The reverse process in which the parameters are computed from the spectrum is usually more difficult and not always unequivocal. Some approximate methods have been developed[22,23] and these may prove very useful. The development of refined spin-decoupling techniques appears feasible and if such methods become available the need for detailed mathematical analysis will be largely circumvented.

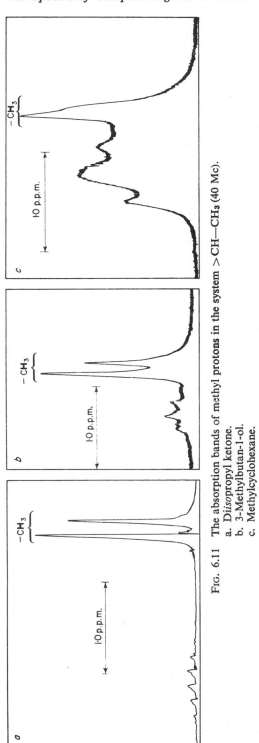

FIG. 6.11   The absorption bands of methyl protons in the system $>CH—CH_3$ (40 Mc).
a. Diisopropyl ketone.
b. 3-Methylbutan-1-ol.
c. Methylcyclohexane.

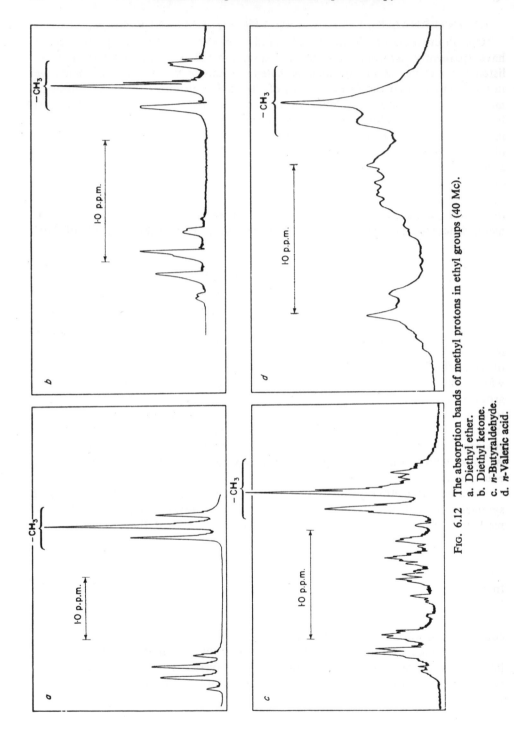

Fig. 6.12   The absorption bands of methyl protons in ethyl groups (40 Mc).
a. Diethyl ether.
b. Diethyl ketone.
c. *n*-Butyraldehyde.
d. *n*-Valeric acid.

6.3 INTERNAL ROTATION AND THE EQUIVALENCE OF NUCLEI

Our discussions of chemical shifts and spin–spin coupling up to this point have frequently involved an implicit assumption. Thus when in Chapter 4 we listed the τ-values of methyl and methylene groups in various environments we in fact assumed that the three protons of the methyl group or the two protons of methylene group were equivalent. We were justified in doing so because the signals from which the τ-values were derived were either single peaks of the correct intensity or multiplets which could only be explained by such equivalence. The observed equivalence of the methyl protons must be a consequence of free rotation about the bond linking the methyl group to the rest of the molecule. A consideration of ethyl iodide will enable us to appreciate this statement. The conformational representation (XVI) of the ethyl iodide molecule shows that in any one conformation there are two protons, *a* and *b*, which are in precisely identical environments different from that of the remaining proton, *c*. Thus if the molecule of ethyl

XVI

iodide was in some way confined to one conformation we would expect only *two* of the methyl protons to be equivalent. However, there are two other conformations which differ only in the labelling of the protons so that if rotation of the methyl group occurs each proton will in turn experience the environment corresponding to *c* in (XVI). Provided the frequency of rotation is rapid compared with the frequency difference between the chemical shifts characteristic of the two possible environments (*c* and *a*, *b*) each proton will experience the same average field. At room temperature methyl groups invariably rotate at rates sufficient to ensure equivalence.

Because the methyl group is unique, in that it possesses a three-fold axis of symmetry coincident with the bond attaching it to the rest of the molecule, the two methylene protons in ethyl iodide will be equivalent even if there is no rotation about the carbon–carbon bond. We have now to inquire whether or not this equivalence of the methylene protons will be maintained if the methyl group is replaced by groups of lower symmetry, such as $—CH(CH_3)_2$ and $—CHBr . CO_2Me$. In order to answer this question we must consider three possible types of rotational behaviour which will depend on the temperature of the system. They are:

(a) Very rapid rotation at high temperature. Under these conditions each conformation will be equally populated.*

(b) Intermediate rates of rotation. Here we assume that the frequency of the interconversion of conformers is high enough to average the environments experienced by the methylene protons but that each conformation is no longer equally populated.

*If we make the assumption that the entropies of each conformation are the same we may write $K = \exp(\Delta E/RT) \rightarrow 1$ as $T \rightarrow \infty$, where K is the constant for the equilibrium between two conformations which differ in energy by ΔE.[23]

(c) Slow or no rotation. Under these conditions each conformer behaves as a stable isomer towards the absorption of radiofrequency radiation.

Let us consider the system —CH_2—CR_2S with reference to an actual example, viz. $BrCH_2CH(Me)_2$. The three conformations are shown below (XVIIa, b, and c). As long as the rotational frequency is high enough to average the shieldings associated with each conformation the two protons (a and b) will be equivalent. This is because the two conformations, (XVIIa) and (XVIIb), in which H_a and H_b are not in equivalent environments, will be identical apart from the labelling of the protons and, since they must be equally populated, rapid interconversion between them will lead to the same average shielding for each proton. At elevated

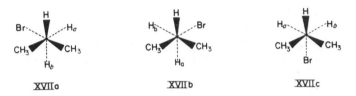

temperatures the populations of the three conformations will approach equality and the shielding of the methylene group becomes the *arithmetic* mean of the three environments. At lower temperatures [behaviour (b)] (XVIIa) and (XVIIb) will increase their populations at the expense of (XVIIc).* The shielding now becomes a *weighted* mean the value of which will be temperature-dependent. The methylene group will still give rise to a single absorption line but the frequency of this line will vary with temperature. At much lower temperatures [behaviour (c)] we may consider the compound as a mixture of two forms. The major component of this mixture will correspond to the identical conformations (XVIIa)

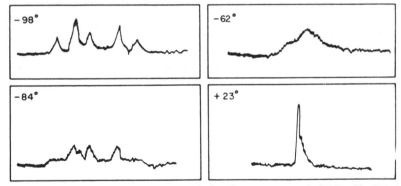

FIG. 6.13   The temperature dependence of the ^{19}F spectrum of CF_2Br-$CbrCN$ (after W. D. Philips[30]).

and (XVIIb) in which the protons are non-equivalent, and will give rise to an **ABX** type spectrum† (p. 90). In the minor component (XVIIc) the methylene protons are equivalent and will therefore result in an A_2X spectrum. An excellent example

*We may predict that this conformation will be the least stable since it has two *gauche* bromine –methyl interactions.

†"X" symbolizes the methine proton of the group —$CH(CH_3)_2$. In the general case, —CR_2S, the type of spectrum observed will depend on the nature of R and S.

of this general behaviour is provided by the fluorine nuclear resonance spectra of $CF_2Br—CBr_2CN$ at various temperatures (Fig. 6.13).[24] We may note that at rotational frequencies intermediate between (b) and (c) the methylene group gives rise to a broad band. This is because average life-times of the conformations are of the same order as the reciprocals of the frequency separations of the two protons so that the shieldings are only partially averaged (p. 28).

We shall now consider the system, $—CH_2—CRST$ in which the methylene group is adjacent to an asymmetric carbon atom. An example is $BrCH_2CBr . CO_2Me$, the three conformations of which are (XVIIIa, b, and c). The first point we notice is

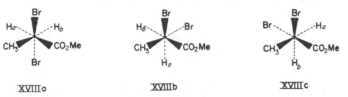

that the environments of H_a in (XVIIIa) and H_b in (XVIIIb) are not necessarily identical because we can see that the non-bonding interactions of the two bromine atoms are quite different in the two conformations and different distortions and polarizations may result in each case. This is a general result which applies for all conformations. We may therefore conclude that even if the groups are rotating so rapidly that the three conformations are equally populated the shielding of H_a is not necessarily equal to that of H_b. At lower temperatures the three conformations will be unequally populated and the non-equivalence of the methylene protons may become more marked. In both cases the methylene protons will give rise to an AB spectrum. At much lower temperatures rotation becomes so slow that the three conformations will absorb as separate species and, in principle, a twelve line spectrum corresponding to three different AB systems is possible. In practice, one or two of the conformations may be insufficiently populated to give rise to signals.

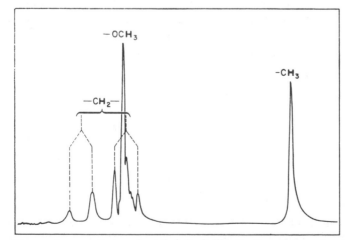

FIG. 6.14   The proton spectrum of methyl 2 : 3-dibromo-2-methylpropionate (40 Mc). (after P. M. Nair and J. D. Roberts[25]).

There is also the possibility of " accidental " equivalence of the proton shieldings. The room temperature spectrum [behaviour (b)] of methyl α : β-dibromoisobutyrate is shown in Fig. 6.14.[25] The results of the study of the fluorine nuclear spectrum of CF_2Br—$CBr(CN)(CH_3)$ at various temperatures carried out by Drysdale and Phillips[26] conform to the general behaviour of the —CH_2—CRST system outlined above. The conclusions regarding the behaviour of various substituted ethanes are summarized in Table 6.4. Pople[27] has given an excellent account of the various types of spectra which are possible for substituted ethanes.

It is obvious that nuclear magnetic resonance spectroscopy will be of great value in studies of rotational barriers and conformational analysis. However, our main interest concerns the way in which conformational effects may enter into the analysis of spectra from which we are attempting to extract structural information. Ethane derivatives usually undergo internal rotation at rates corresponding to behaviour (b) (p. 99) so that non-equivalence of the methylene protons in very simple ethanes only exist if the adjacent group bears three different substituents.*

TABLE 6.4 THE EFFECT OF INTERNAL ROTATION ON THE EQUIVALENCE OF METHYLENE PROTONS IN SUBSTITUTED ETHANES.

System	Equivalence of —CH_2— for the three types of rotational behaviour (see text)		
	(a)	(b)	(c)
—CH_2—CR_3	Equivalent	Equivalent	Equivalent
—CH_2—CR_2S	Equivalent	Equivalent	Non-equivalent.
		Temperature Dependent.	One AB* and one A_2*
—CH_2—CRST	Non-equivalent	Non-equivalent	Non-equivalent
	One AB*	Temperature Dependent. One AB*	Three AB's*

*If R, S or T are magnetic nuclei additional coupling will occur.

We have just seen that the presence of an asymmetric group adjacent to a methylene group can confer non-equivalence of the protons on the latter. There also exists the possibility that asymmetry of more distant groups can produce the same effect. A striking example is provided by the proton spectrum of cortisone acetate (XIX) in which the C_{21} methylene group gives rise to an AB pattern (J_{AB} = 15 c/s; δ_{AB} = 0·15 p.p.m.) near 5·4. Evidently the equivalence of the conformations (XXa) and (XXb) is removed by the asymmetry of the rest of the molecule (R).[28]

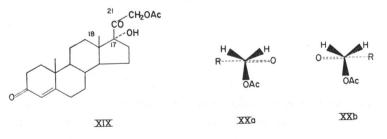

*Nair and Roberts[25] have pointed out that the observation of methylene non-equivalence is not an unequivocal demonstration of the presence of an asymmetric carbon atom. For instance a molecule of the type YCH_2—$C(R)(R')$—CH_2Y will give the same result (see also the next paragraph).

If R is symmetric, as in methoxyacetone, the methylene protons must necessarily be equivalent. Naturally, if the asymmetric group is too far removed or if the asymmetry is slight, the degree to which the methylene protons are non-equivalent may be too small to result in an observable effect. In the case of cortisone acetate the 18-methyl or 17-hydroxyl groups are probably responsible for the distortion of the conformations or for their unequal population.

Some systems rotate sufficiently slowly at room temperature to permit the observation of discrete lines from each conformation. For example dimethylformamide exhibits a doublet near 7·15 which broadens at 140–170° and coalesces to a single band at higher temperatures.[29,30] Similar behaviour has been observed for other amides and also for alkyl nitrites[31,32] and substituted nitrosamines.[33] For all these compounds it is believed that partial double bond character of the bond constituting the axis of rotation, is responsible for the increased stability of the rotational isomers.

We may summarize this section by stating that the equivalence of protons attached to the same carbon atom must never be taken for granted but on the contrary the possibility of non-equivalence should always be in our minds when we are attempting to unravel the spectrum of a complex molecule. Naturally, the non-equivalence of protons attached to the same carbon atom will be more prevalent in molecules which are confined to just one conformation. Thus the axial and equatorial protons of a *trans*-fused decalin are almost always non-equivalent (see Chapter 7).

Finally, we may note that rotation about a single bond can control the magnitude of spin–spin coupling constants across the bond. Thus the free rotation of a methyl group equalizes the three possible coupling constants, J_{AB}, in the system —CH_2—CH_3. If the methyl group is replaced by a group of lower symmetry
    A   B
the coupling constants no longer average to the same value. For instance there are two distinct coupling constants J_{AB} in 1-bromo-2-chloroethane.[12] This is readily understood if it is assumed that the conformation (XXI) predominates at

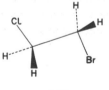

XXI

room temperature [behaviour (b); p. 99] since in this conformation the "*gauche*" and "*staggered*" spin–spin interactions will differ in magnitude.

6.4 LINE POSITIONS

Once the distinction between spin–spin multiplets and chemical shifts has been achieved τ-values can be computed for bands arising from various groups of equivalent protons. The next stage in the analysis of the spectrum is the assignment of each band to an equivalent group of protons in a specific chemical environment. This involves a consideration of intensities and line positions. Finally, a reconsideration of the spin–spin interactions may provide information about the positional relationships of various groups in the molecule. This is, of course, an idealized procedure and frequently many of the absorption bands cannot be assigned. For example, a consideration of the spectrum of 11α-acetoxyprogesterone (Fig. 6.15) leads to the assignment of bands corresponding to only fourteen protons. The signals of the remaining eighteen protons overlap and produce a broad band envelope extending from 7·0 to 9·0. However, even such limited information can be very valuable.

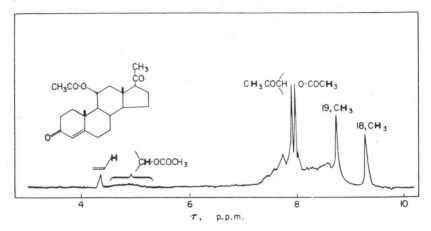

FIG. 6.15   The proton spectrum of 11-α-acetoxyprogesterone.
(after J. N. Shoolery and M. T. Rogers).

The correlation tables in Chapter 4 are a basis for the assignment of structural features from line positions. Their precise function is two-fold. Firstly, they indicate broad regions of absorption associated with the main functional types of protons (e.g. aromatic, olefinic, methoxyl, aldehyde etc.). Secondly, in conjunction with Shoolery's rules they permit reasonably accurate predictions of line positions for protons in acyclic systems. Immediately we depart from acyclic structures we are in some difficulty. We no longer have sufficient data to allow accurate correlations, and furthermore the line positions of nuclei become markedly dependent on induced fields associated with groups which, in terms of bonds, may be quite far removed. Of course as more data become available correlation tables can be extended to cover a greater diversity of structures. At the moment however there are two courses open to us. Firstly, we may establish the line position of a nucleus in a given environment by an examination of carefully chosen model compounds. Secondly we may employ semi-empirical theories which permit the extrapolation of data from acyclic compounds to the type of system under investigation. If line positions are to be used as a proof of structure the examination of model compounds is essential. When comparatively little is known about a structure information derived from line positions most frequently will merely serve as a guide to further chemical studies. At present deductions based on semi-empirical theories of shielding, such as those outlined in the next chapter, must be regarded with considerable caution. Nevertheless, such deductions are useful in that they may limit the selection of likely model compounds or lead to a working hypothesis for subsequent chemical investigations.

6.5 INTENSITIES

If the individual bands in a spectrum are well separated, as is sometimes the case with simple molecules, the determination of their relative intensities provides an estimate of the number of nuclei in each equivalent group. The bands in the spectrum of a complex molecule are seldom sufficiently resolved to enable a complete proton count to be made. However, the numbers of nuclei in those groups which do give rise to discrete bands can be determined and used to provide structural information. The determination of intensities is always a relative procedure and usually involves the comparison of bands within the same spectrum. Thus the number of olefinic protons in mesityl oxide (Fig. 6.1) follows from a comparison of the intensity of the olefinic proton band at 4·03 with the combined intensities of the remaining bands. If we use the same method to estimate the number of olefinic protons in 11α-acetoxyprogesterone (Fig. 6·15) we find that the intensity of the olefinic proton is only 3 per cent of the total so that unless we are very careful we may easily be led into serious errors. In these circumstances it is safer and more convenient to add a known concentration of a reference compound. The spectrum can then be recorded under conditions for which the reference signal and the compound signal give full-scale deflection. The choice of reference will be dictated by the nature of the spectrum under investigation.

Intensity measurements may sometimes be useful for aliphatic C—Me determinations as, unlike the Kuhn–Roth method, they enable a distinction to be made between

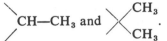

It must be emphasized that accurate intensity measurements require considerable care and strict adherence to the points of technique outlined in Chapter 2.

6.6 EXAMPLES

There are now a number of examples of successful applications of nuclear magnetic resonance spectroscopy to structural problems. Many of these concern the detection of just one structural feature. For example, a decision between structures (XXII) and (XXIII) for Feist's acid is possible on the basis that the spectrum of the diethyl ester has a band at 4·1 equivalent to two protons, attributable only to the group $= CH_2$.[35]

We shall now consider, in detail, two examples which give some indication of the manner in which nuclear magnetic resonance spectroscopy is used in structural work.

$$HO_2C \overset{CH_2}{\underset{XXII}{\triangle}} CO_2H \qquad HO_2C \overset{CH_3}{\underset{XXIII}{\triangle}} CO_2H$$

EXAMPLE 1.[36]

A Reformatsky reaction between 3-methylbut-2-enal and methyl 4-bromo-3-methylbut-2-enoate followed by dehydration of the product afforded two esters, A and B, which analysed for $C_{11}H_{16}O_2$ and exhibited ultraviolet absorption maxima at 280 (ϵ, 24,750) and 230 mμ (ϵ, 22,000), respectively. Possible skeletal arrangements for A are (XXIV) and (XXV), and for B (XXIV)–(XXVII). The nuclear magnetic resonance spectra at 40 Mc of A and B in carbon tetrachloride are shown in Figs. 6.16 and 6.17 respectively.

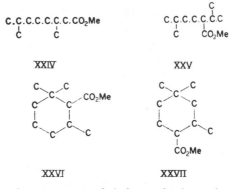

The eight lines in the spectrum of A have the intensity ratio 0·6 : 1·4 : 1·4 : 0·6 : 2 : 2 : 6 : 18. As the ester contains only sixteen protons the first four lines must constitute a pair of spin–spin multiplets arising from an AB spin system. The values of $J_{AB} = 12.0$ c/s and $\delta_{AB} = 48.5$, calculated with the formula given on p. 90, reproduce the observed intensities. The sharp line at 6·35 can be assigned to the $CH_3O.CO$ group (Table 4.5) and the broad band at 8.12 to three allylic methyl groups (Table 4.8). The bands at 4.92 and 5.31 suggest the two protons of a $=CH_2$ group (Table 4.12) one of which must be paramagnetically shielded by a neighbouring group. The breadth of these lines is consistent with a small coupling of the protons with those of substituents at the other end of the double bond. The presence of a terminal methylene group, three allylic methyl groups, and a chromophore absorbing at 280 mμ can only be accommodated by the skeleton (XXV)

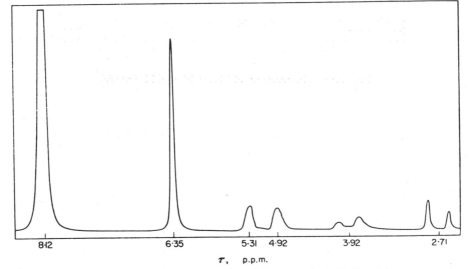

FIG. 6.16   The proton spectrum of "Ester A" in CCl_4 (40 Mc).
The relative intensity of the 8.12 band was determined from a spectrum measured at lower amplification.

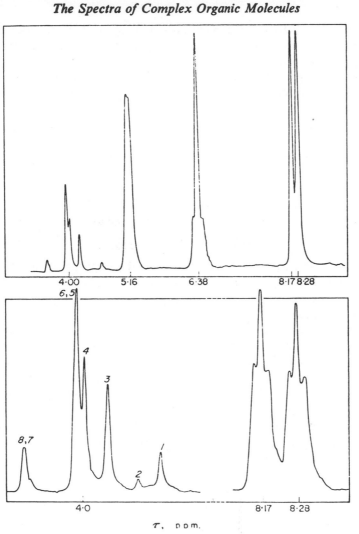

τ, ppm.

FIG. 6.17 The spectrum of "Ester B" in CCl₄ (40 Mc).

and the ester, A, is probably (XXVIII). The doublet at 3.92 can be assigned to the proton at C$_4$ because the individual lines are broadened by coupling with the protons of the isopropylidene residue. The coupling constant J_{AB} has the expected value (Table 6.1) for the system $=CH_A$—$CH_B=$. The stereochemistry indicated in (XXVIII) can be deduced from the τ-values of the doublets on the basis of a theory developed in the next chapter. The same theory will explain the paramagnetic shift of one of the methylene protons, and excludes the double bond isomer of (XXVIII)

XXVIII

The spectrum of B is rather more complex. There are four principal regions of absorption, 8·2, 6·4, 5·16 and 4·65–3·60, which have the intensity ratio 6 : 4 : 4 : 2. The ester methyl line is clearly visible at 6·38 but evidently overlaps another band produced by one proton. This band appears as a broadening at the base of the —OMe signal. The bands at 8·28 and 8·17 can be assigned to two allylic methyl groups. Under high resolution each appears as a triplet with $J \sim 1\cdot0$ c/s suggesting a coupling with à pair of β-olefinic protons. Therefore, each of these bands almost certainly arises from the methyl groups of isopropenyl residues. This assignment is confirmed by the presence of a band at 5·16 ($=CH_2$) equivalent to four protons. Assignments to three protons remain. The complex band (equivalent to two protons) at 4·65–3·62 cannot be a simple AB system since it contains more than four lines, and therefore these three remaining protons must be mutually coupled as an ABX system, the proton X being responsible for the band which is partially hidden under the —OMe line. The AB region of an ABX system usually consists of eight lines but a six line spectrum is consistent with certain values of the parameters. If the lines of the AB band are assigned as shown in Fig. 6.17 (cf. p. 90 and ref. 12) the following values for the four parameters are obtained: $\delta_{AB} = 13\cdot5$ c/s; $J_{AB} = 15\cdot5$ c/s; $J_{AX} = -2\cdot0$ c/s; $J_{BX} = 9\cdot2$ c/s.* These values reproduce the intensities satisfactorily. The τ-values of the A and B protons (4·21 and 3·85) and the magnitude of J_{AB} (cf. Table 6.1) show that the AB system consists of two protons of a *trans*-disubstituted ethylene which is *not* conjugated with a carbomethoxy group. This follows from comparison with a suitable model compound, viz. methyl *trans*-crotonate ($\tau_\alpha = 3\cdot83$, $\tau_\beta = 2\cdot96$, and $J_{\alpha\beta} = 15\cdot75$). The presence of a *trans*-disubstituted ethylene and two isopropenyl groups can only be accommodated by the skeleton (XXV) so that B must have the structure (XXIX). This conclusion is supported by the ultraviolet light absorption of the ester. The protons A and B can be placed at C_4 and C_3 respectively on the grounds that the magnitude of J_{AX} is less than that of J_{BX}. The relative signs of J_{AX} and J_{BX} are not unexpected[36,37] and the rather large value of J_{BX} is probably associated with the fact that the molecule will largely exist in the conformation shown in (XXIX) in which H_B and H_X are staggered (p. 84). The predicted shape of the X band is a doublet with a separation of 7·2 c/s a value approximately equal to the breadth of the lower part of the 6·38 signal.

XXIX

EXAMPLE 2[37]

Spirilloxanthin, a carotenoid isolated from certain sulphur producing bacteria, has been shown to have the molecular formula $C_{42}H_{60}O_2$ and visible light absorption characteristic of a linear polyene containing thirteen conjugated double bonds. Oxidation of spirilloxanthin afforded bixin dial (XXX) and a related polyene

*Because of the degeneracy in the AB spectrum this set is unequivocal apart from the signs of the three coupling constants. The relative signs of J_{AX} and J_{BX} are however correct.

dialdehyde containing two extra double bonds.[38] A Zeisel determination[38] and the infrared spectrum[37] of spirilloxanthin indicate the presence of two aliphatic methoxyl groups. These observations allow the formulation of only two polyene units (**A** and **B**) which are consistent with the fact that spirilloxanthin is derived *in vivo* from lycopene (**XXXI**).[39]

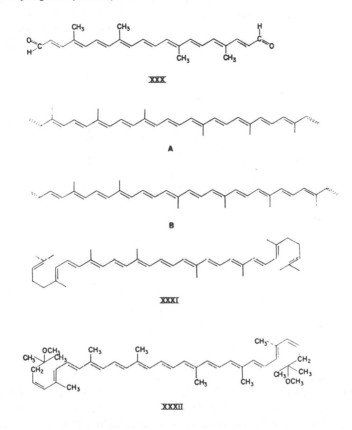

The proton magnetic resonance spectrum in the region 5·0–10·0 is shown in Fig. 6.18. The examination of a large number of carotenoids has demonstrated that a methyl group attached to a terminal carbon atom of a polyene chain absorbs between 8·10 and 8·40. The absence of a band in this region of the spectrum of spirilloxanthin leads to the rejection of the partial formula **B**. The problem is therefore reduced to one of establishing the nature of the end groups which may or may not be the same.

The intensity ratio (from low to high frequencies) of the lines in the spectrum is 6 : 2 : 2 : 18 : 12. The lines at 6·78 and 8·02 therefore confirm the presence of two methoxyl groups and six non-terminal, chain methyl groups, respectively. The sharp line at 8·83 can only be assigned to four aliphatic methyl groups. As this line shows no evidence of multiplicity these groups must be attached to fully substituted carbon atoms and furthermore they must be in very similar, if not equivalent, environments. As there is no absorption between 5·0 and 7·0, apart from the methoxyl line, the two methoxyl groups must also be attached to fully substituted carbon atoms. Consideration of these facts and of the τ-value of the aliphatic methyl groups (Table 4.3) leads to the conclusion that the end groups contain two $(CH_3)_2C(OMe)$-residues. The separation of the pair of lines near 7·70 is unaltered in the spectrum determined at 60 Mc, so that these lines must be a spin–spin doublet ($J = 6·8$ c/s) and as their intensity is equivalent to four protons the band is clearly due to two methylene groups in identical environments. An unequivocal structure (XXXII) for spirilloxanthin can now be written. This structure accounts for both the multiplicity and position of the methylene band.

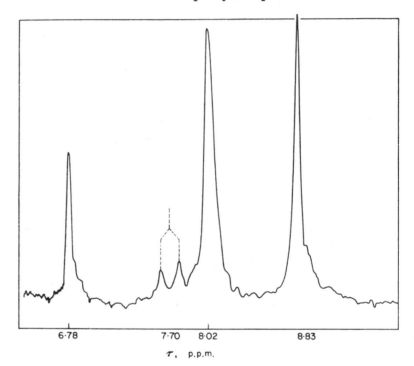

6·78   7·70   8·02   8·83

τ,   p.p.m.

Fig. 6.18   The proton spectrum of spirilloxanthin in $CHCl_3$ (40 Mc).

The multiplicity arises from coupling of each pair of methylene protons with an adjacent olefinic proton. The τ-value of the methylene group in the system $C{=}CH{-}CH_2{-}CH_3$ is found, by application of Shoolery's rules (p. 59), to be 7·83. The observation of a slightly lower value for the methylene groups in spirilloxanthin is consistent with the positions of the methoxyl groups.

REFERENCES

1. W. von E. Doering, G. Laber, R. Vonderwahl, N. F. Chamberlain and R. B. Williams, *J. Am. Chem. Soc.* **78**, 5448 (1956).
2. L. M. Jackman and R. H. Wiley, *Proc. Chem. Soc.* 196 (1958).
3. J. A. Pople, *Mol. Phys.* **1**, 216 (1958).
4. N. Muller, P. C. Lauterbur and G. F. Svatos, *J. Am. Chem. Soc.* **79**, 1807 (1957).
5. A. A. Bothner-By, C. Naar-Colin and B. L. Shapiro, *N.M.R. Spectra and Structure Correlations*, Vol. II, Havard, 1958.
6. M. Karplus, *J. Chem. Phys.* **30**, 11 (1959).

7. R. V. LEMIEUX, R. K. KULLNIG, H. J. BERNSTEIN, W. G. SCHNEIDER, *J. Am. Chem. Soc.* **80** 6098 (1958).
8. W. A. ANDERSON, *Phys. Rev.* **102**, 151 (1956).
9. L. M. JACKMAN, Unpublished results.
10. C. M. SHARTS and J. D. ROBERTS, *J. Am. Chem. Soc.* **79**, 1008 (1957).
11. J. A. ELVIDGE, *J. Chem. Soc.* 474 (1959).
12. H. J. BERNSTEIN, J. A. POPLE and W. G. SCHNEIDER, *Canad. J. Chem.* **35**, 65 (1957).
13. E. L. HAHN and D. E. MAXWELL, *Phys. Rev.* **88**, 1070 (1952).
14. R. E. RICHARDS and T. SCHAEFER, *Molecular Phys.* **1**, 331 (1958).
15. H. M. McCONNELL, A. D. McLEAN and C. A. REILLY, *J. Chem. Phys.* **23**, 1152 (1955).
16. R. E. RICHARDS and T. P. SCHAEFER, *Trans. Faraday. Soc.* **54**, 1280 (1958).
17. R. J. ABRAHAM, J. A. POPLE and H. J. BERNSTEIN, *Canad. J. Chem.* **36**, 1302 (1958).
18. W. G. SCHNEIDER, H. J. BERNSTEIN and J. A. POPLE *ibid.* **35**, 1487 (1957).
19. R. E. RICHARDS and T. SCHAEFER, *Proc. Roy. Soc.* **A246**, 429 (1958).
20. C. NAAR-COLIN and A. BOTHNER-BY, *M.E.L.L.O.N.M.R.* No. 2, p. 14. Issued from the Mellon Institute, 1958.
21. E. B. WILSON, *J. Chem. Phys.* **27**, 60 (1957).
22. J. T. ARNOLD, *Phys. Rev.* **102**, 136 (1956).
23. H. PRIMAS, *Spectrochim. Acta* **14**, 17 (1959).
24. W. D. PHILLIPS, *Ann. New York Acad. Sci.* **70**, 817 (1958).
25. P. M. NAIR and J. D. ROBERTS, *J. Am. Chem. Soc.* **79**, 4565 (1957).
26. J. J. DRYSDALE and W. D. PHILLIPS, *ibid.* 319.
27. J. A. POPLE, *Molecular Phys.* **1**, 3 (1958).
28. J. N. SHOOLERY and M. T. ROGERS, *J. Am. Chem. Soc.* **80**, 5121 (1958).
29. H. S. GUTOWSKY, *Discuss. Faraday Soc.* **19**, 247 (1955).
30. W. D. PHILLIPS, *J. Chem. Phys.* **23**, 1363 (1955).
31. L. H. PIETTE, J. D. RAY and R. A. OGG, *ibid.* **26**, 1341 (1957).
32. W. D. PHILLIPS, C. E. LOONEY and C. P. SPAETH, *J. Molecular Spectroscopy* **1**, 35 (1957).
33. C. E. LOONEY, W. D. PHILLIPS and E. L. REILLY, *J. Am. Chem. Soc.* **79**, 6136 (1957).
34. J. N. SHOOLERY, Varian Associates, *Technical Bulletin*, Vol. 2. No. 3.
35. M. G. ETTLINGER and F. KENNEDY, *Chem. and Ind.* 166 (1956).
36. R. H. WILEY, P. VEERAVAGU, R. P. HOUGHTON and L. M. JACKMAN, Unpublished results.
37. J. A. ELVIDGE and L. M. JACKMAN, *Proc. Chem. Soc.* 89 (1959).
38. S. ALEXANDER, *J. Chem. Phys.* **28**, 358 (1958).
39. M. S. BARBER, L. M. JACKMAN and B. C. L. WEEDON, *Proc. Chem. Soc.* 96 (1959).
40. P. KARRER and H. KOENIG, *Helv. Chim. Acta.* **23**, 460 (1940).
41. S. L. JENSEN, J. COHEN-BAZIRE, R. O. M. NAKAYAMA and R. Y. STANIER, *Biochem. Biophys. Acta.* **29**, 477 (1958).

CHAPTER 7

DIAMAGNETIC ANISOTROPY AND STEREOCHEMISTRY

A NUMBER of observed effects, such as the abnormal shielding of certain methylene groups in polymethylene benzenes (p. 18), the difference between the shielding of methylene groups in cyclic and acyclic systems (p. 51), and the dependence of the frequencies of protons in substituted ethanes on the populations of conformations, suggest that the shielding of a proton may be controlled not only by the nature of neighbouring groups but also by their orientation with respect to the proton. We are thus led to consider possible applications of nuclear magnetic resonance spectroscopy to investigations of stereochemical problems. Our approach, as hitherto, will be largely empirical but we shall also consider certain theories of magnetic shielding which, in some circumstances, lead to useful qualitative predictions.

7.1. LONG RANGE SHIELDING

Let us consider that contribution to the shielding of a proton which arises from a group of electrons, G, not directly associated with the proton. In the hypothetical case in which G consists of the electrons of an isolated atom* the induced field associated with G arises solely from the local diamagnetic circulations of G (p. 15). Because in this case G is spherically symmetrical the induced field is independent of the direction of the applied field. However, the component of the induced field at the proton will depend on the relative orientation of the proton and G with respect to the direction of the applied field. This is shown in Fig. 7.1. If the relative orientations of the proton and G vary in a random fashion over a period of time, as would be the case if they were part of the same molecule in the liquid or gaseous state, it can be shown that the average field produced by G at the proton is zero. In other words, if the induced field of G is isotropic it will not contribute to the shielding of the proton. If G is not spherically symmetrical the strength of its induced field will no longer be independent of the direction of the applied field so that the component of the induced field at the proton, when averaged over all orientations, will have a finite value. We thus conclude that a group of electrons can only contribute to the shielding of a remote proton if the group is magnetically anisotropic. Long range shielding effects are therefore best discussed in terms of diamagnetic anisotropies of groups of electrons.

For the moment we shall confine our attention to a specific example, *viz.* the long range shielding arising from a carbon–carbon triple bond. We saw in Chapter 2 (p. 17) that the triple bond is most readily polarized if the direction of the applied field is coincident with the axis of the bond. In other words if we could measure the diamagnetic susceptibilities of two samples of acetylene, one in which all the molecules were arranged parallel to the main field and the other in which they were

*We assume the atom has a closed shell configuration so that there is no resultant electron spin.

all perpendicularly orientated, we would obtain two different values, the first being the greater. These two values are known as the longitudinal (X_L) and transverse (X_T) susceptibilities, respectively, and their difference (X_L-X_T) is a measure of the diamagnetic anisotropy of acetylene. Now, we know from the classical researches of Pascal[1] that the molar diamagnetic susceptibility is an additive and constitutive

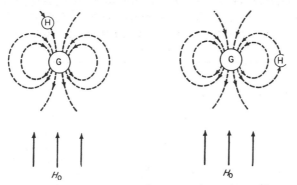

FIG. 7.1 The dependence of the shielding of a proton by an isotropic group of electrons, G, on the relative orientation of the proton and G with respect to the applied field, H_0.

property so that the triple bond is associated with a constant diamagnetic susceptibility irrespective of its molecular environment. It is therefore reasonable to assume that the diamagnetic anisotropy of the triple bond is likewise insensitive to molecular environment[2] so that if we can relate the quantity (X_L-X_T) to the strength and direction of the averaged induced field of the triple bond, we will have a means of determining the contribution which this field makes to the shielding of a remote proton. An approximate relation for an axially symmetrical group of electrons, G, has been derived by McConnell[3] and may be written as

$$\sigma_{av.}(G) = \frac{(3\cos^2\theta-1)(X_L-X_T)}{3r^3} \tag{1}$$

in which r is the distance between the proton and the electrical centre of gravity of G (in the present case the mid-point of the triple bond) and θ is the acute angle

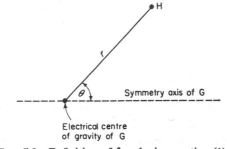

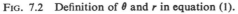

FIG. 7.2 Definition of θ and r in equation (1).

which r makes with the symmetry axis (see Fig. 7.2). The subscript "av." is included to indicate that the shielding has been averaged over all orientations of the system so that equation (1) is directly related to measurements made on liquids or gases.

The graph of the function $(3\cos^2\theta-1)$ vs. θ is shown in Fig. 7.3 and we may note that the value of the function changes sign at $\theta = 55°\ 44'$ so that a carbon–carbon triple bond can either shield or deshield a neighbouring proton depending on their relative orientations. There are in fact two conical regions extending from each end of the triple bond, within which the shielding is positive; outside these regions the shielding is negative (Fig. 7.4). The positions of the protons in acetylene itself correspond to $\theta = 0°$ and, as $\chi_L > \chi_T$, equation (1) predicts a positive shielding contribution from the triple bond in agreement with the high τ-value noted earlier (p. 51).

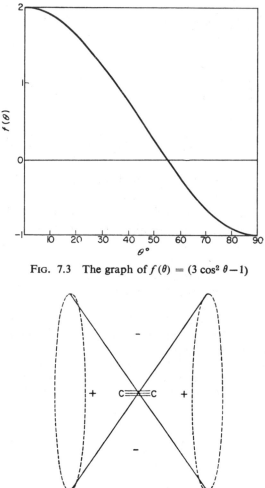

Fig. 7.3   The graph of $f(\theta) = (3\cos^2\theta-1)$

Fig. 7.4   The long range shielding effect of the carbon–carbon triple bond.
    N.B. It is important to realize that this diagram shows only the *sign* of the shielding. The *magnitude* in each region increases towards the symmetry axis of the region, and towards the electrical centre of gravity of the bond.

We must emphasize the approximate nature of equation (1). This equation assumes that the induced field associated with the triple bond (or, in general, the group *G*) can be adequately represented by an infinitesimally small magnet (called a point dipole) at the centre of the triple bond. In other words the finite volume occupied by the electron cloud is ignored. The point dipole approximation is reasonably accurate for large distances. Unfortunately, the distance enters the shielding equation as r^{-3} so that we are primarily concerned with values for which the point dipole approximation is invalid. For this reason we do not expect equation (1) to lead to accurate shielding values but we may still hope that it will provide useful qualitative or even semi-quantitative information.*

Equation (1) is applicable to any single or triple bond or, more generally, to any bond the diamagnetic susceptibility of which can be described in terms of two principal susceptibilities, although for polar bonds the location of the electrical centre of gravity will be uncertain. The anisotropy of a bond or group may arise from either internuclear diamagnetic circulations or from local paramagnetic circulations (p. 16) and $(\chi_L - \chi_T)$ may be either positive or negative. The anisotropy of benzene which arises from the internuclear circulations of the π-electrons can also be described in terms of a longitudinal and a transverse susceptibility. In this case equation (1) is a very poor approximation since it is equivalent to placing the point dipole at the centre of the benzene ring whereas the induced field actually originates above and below the periphery of the aromatic ring. More refined treatments of this problem allow for the shape of the electron cloud and permit the direct calculation of the shielding due to the π-electron circulations.[3,5,6,7,8] No simple formulae can be given but σ_{av} (benzene) has been tabulated,[†5] and represented graphically[8] for the region of space around the benzene ring, and such data permit a reasonably reliable prediction of the shielding due to ring currents provided the geometry of the system is known.

The description of the anisotropy of a double bond in principle requires three mutually perpendicular susceptibilities, χ_L, χ_T and $\chi_\perp$. If $\chi_T \sim \chi_\perp$, equation (1) may still be used for qualitative predictions.

In general, the values of χ_L and χ_T for any group, G, can seldom be directly measured but the quantity $(\chi_L - \chi_T)$ can be determined, within the limits imposed by the assumptions involved in equation (1), from nuclear magnetic resonance data for suitable model compounds.[9]

7.2 THE STEREOCHEMISTRY OF CYCLOHEXANE AND RELATED RING SYSTEMS

There is abundant evidence that the axial and equatorial protons of cyclo-hexane and its derivatives are not equally shielded. Of course in cyclohexane itself the two chair conformations are equally populated and are interchanging so rapidly that the shielding of all protons is averaged to a single value (p. 51). In other systems in which one conformation predominates or in which interchange of conformations is impossible (as in the *trans*-decalin system) separate signals for

*It may be possible to refine equation (1) by using a uniformly polarized sphere approximation (or some similar device) as has been done for the approximate evaluation of electron repulsion integrals.[4]

†In the treatment by Waugh and Fessenden σ_{av} (benzene) $= 15\cdot9 \times 10^{-14} \times B_0(\rho, z)$ where B_0 is tabulated for various values of ρ and z. The definitions of ρ and z are given in the annexed diagram and are expressed in units of a where $a = 1\cdot4 \times 10\,cm^{-8}$.

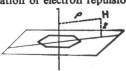

axial and equatorial protons may be observed. Table 7.1 lists the difference, δ_{ae}, between the τ-values of axial and equatorial protons for several compounds and pairs of compounds for which the comparison is possible. In each case *the axial proton absorbs at higher frequencies than its equatorial counterpart*. Lemieux,

TABLE 7.1 RELATIVE CHEMICAL SHIFTS OF AXIAL
AND EQUATORIAL PROTONS

Compounds	δ_{ae} (p.p.m.)
δ-1:2:3:4:5:6-Hexachlorocyclohexane[10]	0·51
ϵ-1:2:3:4:5:6-Hexachlorocyclohexane[10]	0·20
myo-Inositol hexaacetate[10]	0·20
cis and *trans* 4-tert-Butylcyclohexanol[10]	0·13
cis and *trans* 4-tert-Butylcyclohexyl acetate[10]	0·40
Androsterone and *epi*androsterone[11]	0·45
11α- and 11β-Hydroxyprogesterone[11]	0·43

Kullnig, Schneider, and Bernstein[10] have found that this rule is also obeyed by a number of anomeric pairs of pyranose sugar acetates (Table 7.2). The spectrum of β-D-xylopyranose tetraacetate (1) has provided particularly elegant demonstration of the different shielding of axial and equatorial protons.[10] The two protons at C_5 form the AB portion of an ABX spin system (p. 90) and an analysis of the appropriate band in the spectrum has revealed a chemical shift, δ_{AB}, of 0·65 p.p.m. between the axial and equatorial protons; a consideration of the magnitudes of the coupling constants, J_{AX} and J_{BX} (p. 84) has shown that the equatorial proton absorbs at the lower frequency.

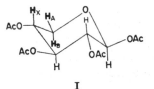

I

TABLE 7.2 RELATIVE CHEMICAL SHIFTS (p.p.m.) FOR THE ANOMERIC
PROTONS OF α AND β ACETYLATED ALDOPYRANOSES

Compound	δ_{ae}
α- and β-D-Glucose pentaacetates	0·45
α- and β-D-Galactose pentaacetates	0·63
α- and β-D-Mannose pentaacetates	0·29
α- and β-D-Xylose tetraacetates	0·64
α- and β-D-Ribose tetraacetates	0·10
α-L- and -β-D-Arabinose tetraacetates	0·68

It is obvious that the chemical shift, δ_{ae}, between axial and equatorial protons must have its origin in a long range shielding effect associated with the diamagnetic anisotropy of the carbon–carbon single bonds.* Bothner-By and Naar-Colin[9]

*For reasons stated earlier (p. 17) the contribution from C—H bonds will be neglibible.

have computed the value of $(\chi_L - \chi_T)$ for the carbon–carbon single bond by assuming that the difference of 0·06 p.p.m. between the τ-values for the protons in cyclohexane and cyclopentane can be explained in terms of equation (1). Their value of $-5·5 \times 10^{-30}$ cm³/molecule may be inaccurate but is probably of the correct order. The negative sign indicates that the transverse magnetic polarizability of the carbon–carbon single bond is greater than its longitudinal magnetic polarizability and Bothner-By and Naar-Colin have argued that this should be true for many single bonds.[2] The shielding arising from single bonds must therefore be the reverse in sign of that indicated for the triple bond (Fig. 7.3). These conclusions are in agreement with the observed difference in the shielding of the axial and equatorial protons in cyclohexane systems as we shall now indicate with reference to Fig. 7.5A. The C_1—C_2 and C_1—C_6 bonds are symmetrically orientated with respect to the two protons at C_1 and will consequently make an equal contribution to the shielding of each. The 2:3 bond on the other hand bears a different spatial relation to each proton. Thus for the equatorial proton $\theta = 31°$ and $r = 2·8 \times 10^{-8}$ cm. The same values apply to the 5:6 bond. The corresponding values for the axial proton are $r = 2·35 \times 10^{-8}$ cm and $\theta = 67°$. Equation (1) then tells us that the equatorial proton will be deshielded by the 2:3 and 5:6 bonds whereas the axial proton will be shielded. Using the value of $-5·5 \times 10^{-30}$ cm³ for $(\chi_L - \chi_T)$ we obtain 0·40 p.p.m. for the difference in τ-values of the axial and equatorial protons. This is in surprisingly good agreement with the values of δ_{ae} quoted in Table 7.1. We could of course allow for the effects of the 3:4 and 4:5 bonds which shield both protons but to different extents. However the contribution of these bonds is quite small even though it is unduly weighted by equation (1).*

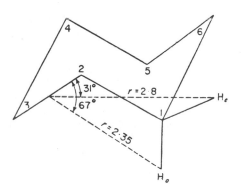

FIG. 7.5A   Long range shielding in cyclohexane.

The fact that δ_{ae} has similar values for cyclohexane protons and protons at C_2 and C_6 in the pyran ring (Tables 7.1 and 7.2) suggests that the magnetic anisotropy of the carbon–oxygen single bond is similar to that of the carbon–carbon single bond. The uncertainty in the location of the electrical centre of gravity of the former bond precludes a quantitative comparison of $(\chi_L - \chi_T)$ for the two types.

A qualitative prediction of the shielding contributions of substituents in rigid

*This is a consequence of the point dipole approximation.

cyclohexane or pyran ring systems is now possible. An equatorial substituent at C_2 and C_5 (Fig. 7.5A) will effect both axial and equatorial protons (C_1) alike and should therefore leave δ_{ae} unchanged. An axial substituent at C_2 (or C_5) on the other hand is expected to nullify the shielding contribution of the 2:3 (or 5:6) bond as is best seen by viewing the environments of the two protons in the direction of the 1:2 bond (Fig. 7.5B). A 2-axial substituent should therefore reduce δ_{ae}. An axial

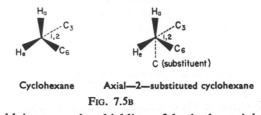

Cyclohexane   Axial—2—substituted cyclohexane

FIG. 7.5B

substituent at C_3 should increase the shielding of both the axial and equatorial protons at C_1 but since the axial proton is nearer the substituent, an increase in δ_{ae} is predicted. The inadequacies of the point dipole approximation do not permit a reliable estimate of the magnitude of this effect. An equatorial substituent at C_3 and axial and equatorial substituents at C_4 are probably too far removed to make a significant contribution to the shielding of protons at C_1. Unfortunately, there are no available data for rigid systems with which we can check these conclusions. We can however seek explanations for the low values of δ_{ae} observed for the ribose tetraacetates and mannose pentaacetates (Table 7.2). In the case of the ribose derivatives the low value of δ_{ae} almost certainly indicates that the β-isomer is a mixture of the conformations (II) and (III) the latter possibly predominating. On the other hand the values (3 c/s) of the coupling constants J_{AX} (see formulae) for α and β mannose pentaacetates suggest that these epimers exist predominantly in the conformations (IV) and (V), respectively, so the low value of δ_{ae} may well be due to the influence of the axial substituent at C_2.

Clearly the above discussion does little more than suggest a promising approach to the problem of elucidating the role of long-range shielding effects in cyclohexane derivatives and related systems, and a number of critical experiments are required to establish the utility of proton chemical shifts for conformational analysis of

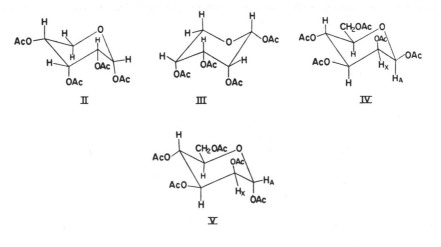

cyclic systems. We may note at this stage that the assumed diamagnetic anisotropy of the carbon–carbon single bond accounts quite well for the fact that the frequencies of both aliphatic and olefinic protons are shifted to lower frequencies by increased alkylation of the carbon atom to which the proton is attached. For example, methylene groups in straight chain alkanes absorb at frequencies some 0.35 p.p.m. lower than found for aliphatic methyl groups and the shift calculated from equation (1), using the value of -5.5×10^{-30} for $(\chi_L - \chi_T)$ for the carbon–carbon single bond, is 0.32 p.p.m.[9] Similarly the computed differences in the τ-values of the olefinic protons in isobutylene and 2-methylbut-2-ene are 0.46 compared with the experimental value of 0.60 p.p.m.[13]

7.3. GEOMETRICAL ISOMERISM ABOUT CARBON–CARBON DOUBLE BONDS

We shall first consider the contribution which *cis* and *trans* β-substituents make to the shielding of an olefinic proton in simple derivatives of ethylene. An ideal approach to this subject would be to study the shielding of the olefinic protons in a series of simple monosubstituted ethylenes. However, the olefinic protons of such compounds give rise to complicated ABC or ABX patterns and few data are as yet available in the literature. We shall therefore base our discussion mainly on the spectra of 1:1-disubstituted ethylenes of the type (VI) and *cis-trans* pairs of substituted ethylenes.*

VI

We first require a value for the contribution of the C—Me bond to the shielding of the two olefinic protons of (VI). Equation (1) suggests that this bond should shield the proton $H_{(trans)}$ and deshield $H_{(cis)}$ but that the resultant chemical shift should be quite small (*ca.* 0.1 p.p.m.). There is some experimental confirmation of these conclusions. Thus, Alexander[13] has shown that the frequency difference between the two terminal olefinic protons in both but-1-ene and 3:3-dimethylbut-1-ene is 0.1 p.p.m. and the values of the coupling constants for the second compound indicate that the proton which is *cis* to the alkyl group absorbs at the higher frequency [this proton corresponds to $H_{(trans)}$ in the formula (VI)]. However, in both these compounds there is the possibility of shielding contributions from other carbon–carbon single bonds. An indirect determination of the shielding contribution of the C—Me bond to $H_{(cis)}$ and $H_{(trans)}$ in (VI) can be obtained from the τ-values of the olefinic protons in isopropenyl bromide and *cis*- and *trans*-dibromoethylene. The τ-values of *cis*- and *trans*-dibromoethylene are 3.00 and 3.38 respectively[12] so that δ_{tc} (defined as $\tau_{trans} - \tau_{cis}$ where *cis* and *trans* refer to the relation of X to H) is -0.38 p.p.m. Comparison of this value with 0.20 p.p.m., which is the difference in the chemical shifts of the two olefinic protons in isopropenyl bromide (VI; X = Br), yields the value of $+0.18$ p.p.m. for the contribution of

---

*Unless otherwise stated, the data and theories given in this section are the results of investigations by Professor R. H. Wiley and the author.

the C—Me bond to the difference in shielding between the olefinic protons in (VI). Thus where $X = CH_3$, δ_{tc} must be —0·18 p.p.m.

The separations of the two olefinic protons in (VI) for various substituents, X, are given in Table 7.3 together with the values of δ_{tc}. The values of δ_{tc} have been computed using δ_{tc} for the C—Me bond equal to —0·15 p.p.m. and in general two values are obtained for each substituent since the sign of the difference between the two proton frequencies is undetermined. The sign and hence the correct value of δ_{tc} can be obtained from the study of *cis–trans* pairs of compounds of the type —CH=CX—.

TABLE 7.3 THE DIFFERENTIAL SHIELDING OF *cis* AND *trans* OLEFINIC PROTONS BY β-SUBSTITUENTS

Substituent, X	Separation (p.p.m.) of the olefinic proton frequencies in (VI)	δ_{tc} (p.p.m.) for X*	
—CH₃	(0·00)	(—0·15)	
—CH₂C(CH₃)₃	0·175	+0·325	—0·025
—Br	0·20		—0·35
—CN	*ca.* 0·05	0·20	—0·10
—CO₂Me	0·50	+0·35	
—CONH₂	0·40	+0·20	
—COCl	0·44	+0·24	
—COMe	0·20	+0·05	
—CHO	0·275	+0·125	
—Ph	0·26	+0·11	
—OAc	0·05	0·20	—0·10

* Only one value is given if the sign of δ_{tc} can be inferred from data for *cis–trans* pairs.

We can now proceed in the same way to determine the contribution which a β-substituent makes to the shielding of a methyl group attached to an ethylenic double bond. Suitable models in this case are of the type (VII). We do not expect

VII

to observe such large effects in this system since the shielding by the substituent X has to be averaged over all three conformations of the methyl group. As we do not anticipate a long range shielding from the olefinic C—H bond the magnitude of δ_{tc} is determined uniquely but the sign is again uncertain unless data for appropriate *cis–trans* pairs are available. The results of a survey of a number of compounds of the type (VII) are listed in Table 7.4.

The data in Tables 7.3 and 7.4 indicate that nuclear magnetic resonance spectroscopy may be a valuable technique for assigning configurations to ethylenic isomers, particularly when the compounds are tri- and tetra-substituted ethylenes for such cases are often difficult to handle by other methods. It is also apparent from the tables that the shielding by some substituent groups arises from an anisotropy of the group itself rather than from the electrons which bind it to the ethylenic carbon atom. This is particularly true if the substituent is a phenyl group or if it contains a carbonyl group conjugated with the double bond presumably because of the large diamagnetic anisotropies of these groups (pp. 17, 18).

TABLE 7.4 THE DIFFERENTIAL SHIELDING OF THE PROTONS OF *cis* AND *trans* METHYL GROUPS BY β-SUBSTITUENTS

Substituent, X	Separation (p.p.m.) of methyl proton frequencies	δ_{tc} (p.p.m.) for X*
—H	(0·00)	(0·00)
—CH₃	0·00	0·00
—C(CH₃)₃	0·06	±0·06
—Br	0·00	0·00
—C⫶CH	0·10	±0·10
—CO₂Me	0·275	+0·275
—COMe	0·25	+0·25
—CHO	0·20	+0·20
—OAc	0·00	0·00
—CH₂OH	0·00	0·00

* Only one value is given if the sign of δ_{tc} can be inferred from data for *cis–trans* pairs.

The data for several pairs of *cis-* and *trans-*α:β-unsaturated carboxylic esters (Table 7.5) confirm the predictions made above. We may note that the differential shielding of olefinic protons by the carbomethoxy group is considerably larger than indicated in Table 7.3. For instance the differences between the olefinic proton frequencies of methyl methacrylate (VI; X=CO₂Me), and between those of methyl citraconate (VIII) and methyl mesaconate (IX), should be equal. However, the shielding of the olefinic proton in methyl citraconate will be increased if the carbomethoxy group is forced out of co-planarity with the double bond by non-bonding interaction with the methyl group, and, since loss of co-planarity will reduce electron withdrawal from the β-position of the double bond, the contribution of the local diamagnetic effect (p. 16) will be increased.

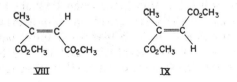

If we take into account the fact that a methyl group is freely rotating we may conclude that the shielding effect of the carbonyl group is greater for a β-methyl proton than for a β-olefinic proton which is in agreement with the fact that the

TABLE 7.5 SHIFTS OF β-OLEFINIC AND β-METHYL PROTON FREQUENCIES
IN *cis–trans* $\alpha:\beta$-UNSATURATED ESTERS

Compounds	$\tau_A - \tau_B$ (p.p.m.)	
	β-Olefinic proton	β-Methyl proton
A Dimethyl maleate B Dimethyl fumarate	0·53	—
A Methyl citraconate B Methyl mesoconate	0·80	0·20
A Methyl *cis*-crotonate B Methyl *trans*-crotonate	0·63	−0·25
A Methyl angelate B Methyl tiglate	0·75	−0·25
A Dimethyl *cis*-β-methylglutoconate B Dimethyl *trans*-β-methylglutoconate	—	0·25
A Dimethyl dimethylmaleate B Dimethyl dimethylfumarate	—	0·10

carbonyl group can more closely approach the former nucleus. It has been suggested that the deshielding effect of the carbonyl group in these systems is due to
weak hydrogen bonding[14] but in view of the very low τ-values of aldehyde protons
it is probable that the anisotropy of the carbonyl group is sufficient to account for
the magnitude of the observed shifts. According to Pople[15] the anisotropy of the
carbonyl group arises from paramagnetic circulations induced by the component
of the applied field in the plane of the trigonal carbon atom. Accordingly, the
largest of the three principal susceptibilities will be perpendicular to this plane, i.e.
$\chi_\perp$. This conclusion is borne out by the very elegant experiments of Lauterbur in
which the ^{13}C chemical shifts of the carbonate ion in oriented crystals of calcite
have been determined.[16] We can therefore conclude that the shielding associated
with the carbonyl group will be positive in conical regions extending above and
below the plane of the double bond and negative elsewhere (Fig. 7.6). This is a
very crude picture as it assumes equality of the transverse and longitudinal susceptibilities and places the electrical centre of gravity at the mid-point of the bond
but is near enough for our present purposes and it tells us that deshielding of
protons will be greatest if they lie in the plane of the carbonyl group. Both β-olefinic
and β-methyl protons will be in this plane when they are closest to the carbonyl
group. In other words the carbonyl group will cause maximum deshielding of
β-protons when the molecule is in the planar S-*cis* conformation (X) and we may
expect a correlation between S-*cis* character and the τ-values of these protons.
The data in Table 7.6 provide striking evidence that these ideas are indeed correct.

X

In the view of the above discussion it seems almost certain that the anomalous shielding of the *o*-protons in compounds such as benzaldehyde, acetophenone and methyl benzoate is due to the anisotropy of the carbonyl group rather than to a

TABLE 7.6. THE EFFECT OF CONFORMATION ON THE SHIELDING OF THE β-PROTONS OF α:β-UNSATURATED CARBONYL COMPOUNDS

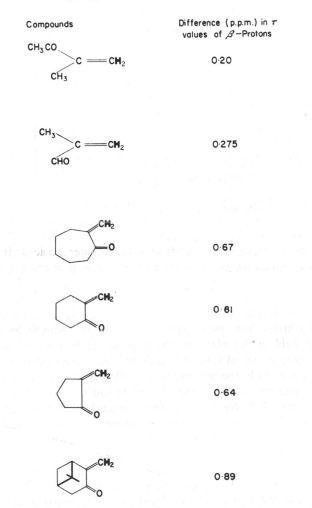

Compounds	Difference (p.p.m.) in τ values of β-Protons
(CH₃CO, CH₃)C=CH₂	0·20
(CH₃, CHO)C=CH₂	0·275
(cycloheptanone =CH₂)	0·67
(cyclohexanone =CH₂)	0·81
(cyclopentanone =CH₂)	0·64
(bicyclic ketone =CH₂)	0·89

specific electrostatic effect (—*I*). Similar shifts are observed with some of the substituted thiophenes listed in Table 4.16 (p. 65), and the substituted furans in Table 4.15.

We have noted that the carbonyl group of an α:β-unsaturated acid can de-shield the protons of a β-methyl group but that the magnitude of the effect is reduced by free rotation of the methyl group. If the β-substituent is another ethylenic bond, as in a diene acid, the freedom of the substituent is greatly reduced and large paramagnetic shifts are observed for the γ-protons. This is well illustrated by the τ-values for the appropriate olefinic protons in the three isomeric dimethyl muconates

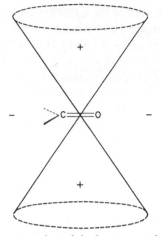

F𝐈𝐆. 7.6   An approximate representation of the long range shielding effect of the carbonyl group.
N.B. See footnote to Fig. 7.4.

(XI), (XII), and (XIII) in which the γ-interaction is seen to be much larger than the β-interaction.[17] In dimethyl *cis–trans* muconate (XIII) one of the protons is deshielded by both carbonyl groups and as a result its absorption is shifted by 1·7 p.p.m. to lower frequencies. Similar results have been observed for the β-methyl- and α:α'-dimethyl muconic acids.[18,19]

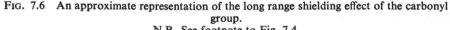

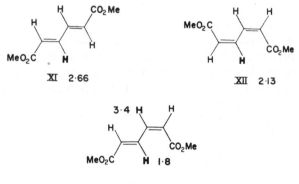

An example which illustrates the value of the concepts outlined in this section is provided by the elucidation of the stereochemistry of the trisubstituted double bond in phytol (XXIV).[19a] It is evident from the data in Table 7.4 that the nuclear

$$\text{(CH}_3)_2\text{CH . (CH}_2)_3 . \overset{\overset{\displaystyle \text{CH}_3}{|}}{\text{CH}} . \text{(CH}_2)_3 . \overset{\overset{\displaystyle \text{CH}_3}{|}}{\text{CH}} . \text{(CH}_2)_3 . \overset{\overset{\displaystyle \text{CH}_3}{|}}{\text{C}} = \text{CH . R}$$

(XXIV); R = CH₂OH
(XXV); R = CO₂Me
(XXVI); R = CHO

magnetic resonance spectra of phytol and its double bond stereoisomer would not allow an assignment of configuration. However, phytol can be transformed into the corresponding aldehyde and thence to the acid by stereospecific methods, and the spectra of these derivatives have been used to establish the stereochemistry of the double bond in phytol itself. A mixture of the geometrically isomeric methyl phytenoates (XXV) was synthesized and a separation of the isomers effected. As expected the spectra of the two esters differed only in the position of the band arising from the vinylic methyl group. This band, a doublet ($J \sim 1{\cdot}0$ c/s) in each case, was found at 8·205 in one ester and 7·85 in the other, the latter clearly corresponding to a *cis* relation between the vinyl methyl and ester groups. Similarly, a mixture of the two isomeric phytenals (XXVI), obtained by manganese dioxide oxidation of a synthetic mixture of *cis-* and *trans-*phytol, exhibited doublets ($J \sim 1{\cdot}0$ c/s) at 8·10 and 7·91, and again the lower value was assigned to a methyl group *cis* to the carbonyl substituent. Natural phytol itself was shown, by gas-liquid chromatography, to be essentially one isomer. On manganese dioxide oxidation the natural alcohol yielded an aldehyde exhibiting a doublet at 7·91, and the methyl ester derived from this aldehyde by silver oxide oxidation followed by esterification with diazomethane had a doublet at 7·85. Natural phytol must therefore be the isomer possessing the geometry in which the carbinol and methyl groups are on the same side of the ethylenic bond. A similar series of transformations has been carried out with nerol and geraniol and the spectra of the aldehydes and acids has established the relationships of the two alcohols to citral *a* and *b* and to the two isomeric geranic acids.[19a]

7.4 EXAMPLES OF LONG RANGE SHIELDING BY THE BENZENE RING

The approximate nature of the induced field which arises from the diamagnetic circulations of the π-electrons of benzene is illustrated in Fig. 7.7 and we may use this diagram to predict the sign of the contribution to the shielding of neighbouring protons. The magnitude of the induced field is such that appreciable effects may be observed for protons as far removed as 5 or 6 Å from the centre of the ring.

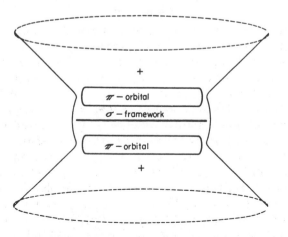

Fig. 7.7   Long range shielding of the benzene ring.
N.B. See footnote to Fig. 7.5. In this case the magnitude increases towards the π-orbitals rather than towards the electrical centre of gravity of the π electrons.

Curtin, Gruen, and Shoulders[20] have examined several pairs of *cis–trans* isomers in which the stereoisomerism involves phenyl substituents and they have observed quite large frequency shifts which arise from long range shielding by the aromatic rings. Thus, the olefinic proton frequencies of *cis-* and *trans-*stilbene [see formulae (XVII) and (XVIII)] indicate that in the *trans* isomer the two rings are essentially coplanar with the double bond and hence deshield the olefinic protons. On the other hand the frequencies of the protons α to the phenyl groups in *trans-* and *cis-* 1:2-dephenyl cyclopentane (XIX) and (XX), show that in both isomers the phenyl groups are not coplanar.

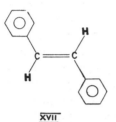

XVII

XVIII

$\tau = 3 \cdot 01$ (each proton lies in the plane of the two phenyl groups and is therefore deshielded).

$\tau = 3 \cdot 51$ (the aromatic rings are tilted and the deshielding of the olefinic protons is therefore reduced).

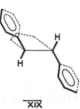

XIX

XX

$\tau = 7 \cdot 11$ (each proton lies *above* the plane of the vicinal phenyl group and is therefore shielded).

$\tau = 6 \cdot 71$ (each proton is further removed from the vicinal phenyl group than in the *trans* isomer and therefore the shielding is less).

The character of the induced field associated with the aromatic ring as depicted in Fig. 7.7 suggests that the frequency of the *ortho*-protons in diphenyl will be a function of the dihedral angle between the planes of the two benzene rings, and that nuclear magnetic resonance spectroscopy might be useful in conformational studies of *ortho*-substituted diphenyls. By using the method of Waugh and Fessenden (p. 115) it is possible to compute the change in the frequency of the *ortho*-protons which accompanies internal rotation in diphenyl and the results of the calculation are given graphically in Fig. 7.8.* The effect of twisting the two rings 90° out-of-plane is to increase the shielding of the *ortho*-protons by approximately 0·40 p.p.m. The dihedral angle of diphenyl in the gas phase is approximately 45°[21] and presumably the value is similar in the liquid phase. The introduction of large *ortho*-substituents such as chlorine, bromine or iodine widen the angle to approximately 70°[22] and should therefore decrease the de-shielding of the *ortho*-protons by the aromatic rings. From Fig. 7.8 the magnitude of this diamagnetic

*These results are based on the more refined model in which the π-electron system is divided into two parts above and below the ring.

shift should be *ca.* 0·25 p.p.m. which is in fair agreement with the observations of Brownstein[23] recorded in Table 7.7. A direct correlation between the diamagnetic shift with the size of the halogen is not possible because the carbon–halogen bonds will also contribute to the shielding of the *ortho*-protons on the adjacent ring and as yet there is no adequate way of allowing for this effect.

TABLE 7.7 THE EFFECT OF *ortho*-SUBSTITUENTS
ON THE FREQUENCIES OF *ortho*-PROTONS IN DIPHENYL

2-Substituent	$\tau_0 - \tau^*{}_{m \text{ and } p}$
F	0·18
Cl	0·21
Br	0·21
I	0·18

* The spectra of these compounds are complex and the assignments cannot be regarded as certain. The spectra of the last three compounds consist of two bands with respective intensity ratios of 2:4·7, 2:5·2 and 2:8·2.

Recently, Goodwin, Shoolery, and Johnson[24] have reported data for dicentrine (XXI) and bulbocapnine (XXII), two alkaloids of the aporphine group possessing diphenyl structures in which the two aromatic rings are confined to a non-planar configuration. As a consequence of the molecular asymmetry of these compounds the protons of the methylene-dioxy-groups are unequally shielded by the aromatic ring A and hence give rise to an AB type spectrum (p. 89; $\delta_{AB} = 0·15–0·20$ p.p.m.; $J_{AB} = 1–2$ c/s). A further point of interest is that the proton at C_4 in dicentrine

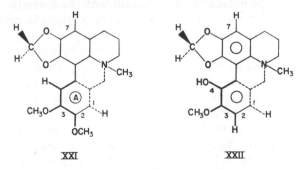

XXI   XXII

absorbs at a much lower frequency than found for the remaining aromatic protons, suggesting that the dihedral angle between the planes of the two aromatic rings is quite small (see Fig. 7.8), although possibly this proton is deshielded by fields associated with the anisotropies of the carbon–oxygen bonds of the methylenedioxy-group.

The theories of internuclear diamagnetic π-electron circulations give a reasonable qualitative account of the proton shifts in polynuclear benzenoid hydrocarbons.[5] In such systems the π-electron charge density is the same at each carbon atom so that the *local* diamagnetic shielding contribution (p. 16) will be identical for each

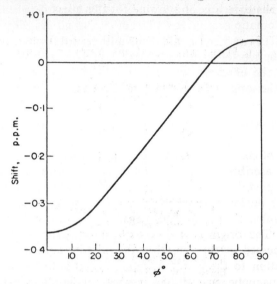

FIG. 7.8   The dependence of the shielding of *o*-protons in diphenyl on the dihedral angle, ϕ, between the planes of the two benze rings.

proton and any difference in shielding must arise from the anisotropies of the π-electron system and of the σ-bonds which constitute the molecular framework, the former presumably being the more important. Qualitatively, we can describe the results of the π-electron theories by saying each ring makes a contribution (not necessarily equal) to the total induced field so that the proton which is nearest to

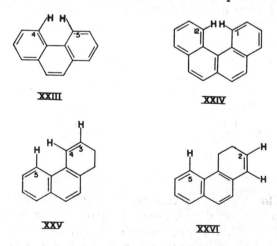

the greatest number of rings will have the lowest frequency. Thus the 4- and 5-protons in phenanthrene (XXIII) are more deshielded than those in the other positions. This effect is most pronounced for the 1- and 12-protons in 3:4-benz-phenanthrene (XXIV) and Reid [25] has suggested that the known steric distortion in this molecule may contribute to the deshielding of the two protons in question. In an effort to separate the effects of internuclear diamagnetic shielding and steric distortion, Reid[26] has compared the frequency differences between the two olefinic protons and the aromatic proton at C_5 in both 1:2- and 3:4-dihydrophenanthrene (XXV) and (XXVI) respectively, and shown that the former effect alone could not account for the shielding of the 4- and 5-protons in (XXV). However, this treatment ignores the effect of conjugation, which may be different in the two isomers, and also the long range shielding of the 5-proton by the double bond (see below).

7.5. THE DIAMAGNETIC ANISOTROPY OF THE CARBON–CARBON DOUBLE BOND

The difference of *ca.* 4 p.p.m. in the shielding of aliphatic and olefinic protons is too large to be ascribed entirely to a difference in local diamagnetic shielding and we are led to postulate a long range contribution from the π-electrons of the double bond to the shielding of olefinic protons. This contribution, like that of the carbon–oxygen double bond, must be negative (i.e. deshielding) in the plane of the double bond. The origin of anisotropy of the carbon–carbon double bond has not been discussed in the literature but as this bond makes a large para-magnetic contribution to the molar susceptibility[1] it is likely that the anisotropy arises from paramagnetic circulations induced by in-plane components of the applied field. We may therefore conclude that the character of the long range shielding associated with the carbon–carbon double bond is similar to that of the carbonyl group (Fig. 7.6).

In agreement with the above conclusion there is evidence that protons which are situated above the plane of an olefinic double bond are abnormally shielded.

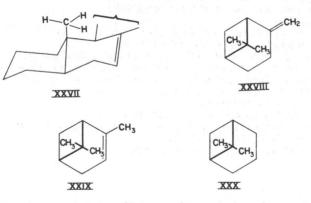

XXVII

XXVIII

XXIX

XXX

For instance, Shoolery and Rogers[11] have observed that the methyl protons at C_{19} in Δ^7-steroids (XXVII) exhibit a diamagnetic shift of 0·10 p.p.m. Similarly a comparison of the spectra of α-pinene (XXVIII) and β-pinene (XXIX) with that of norpinane (XXX) reveals that the frequency of one of the *gem*-methyl groups in both the unsaturated compounds is diamagnetically shifted by 0·20–0·30 p.p.m. In all these examples the magnitudes of the diamagnetic shifts are relatively small presumably as a consequence of the free rotation of the methyl groups.

7.6. A RECONSIDERATION OF SHOOLERY'S RULES

In view of the magnitudes of shifts resulting from long range shielding it is at first sight surprising that Shoolery's rules for methylene groups (p. 59) are as accurate as they seem to be and it appears that a group X must always adopt the same conformation with respect to —CH_2Y regardless of the nature of Y. This is probably true because Y will always be larger than the two protons so that one conformation about the X—CH_2Y bond will be preferred whatever the nature of Y. For systems of the type X—CHYZ the population of conformations arising from rotation about the C—X bond will depend on the relative sizes of Y and Z and the long range shielding by X may vary from compound to compound. These considerations do not apply in cases where X is an atom or a linear group and the anomalous variation of the τ-values of α-protons in alkyl halides must have a different explanation (p. 54).

REFERENCES

1. A. PASCAL, references listed in *Jahrb. d. Rad. und. Elektr.* **17**, 184 (1920).
2. A. A. BOTHER-BY and C. NAAR-COLIN, *J. Am. Chem. Soc.* **80**, 1728 (1958).
3. H. M. McConnell, *J. Chem. Phys.* **27**, 226 (1957).
4. R. PARISER and R. G. PARR, *ibid.* **21**, 466 (1953).
5. A. J. BERNSTEIN, W. G. SCHNEIDER, and J. A. POPLE, *Proc. Roy. Soc. A.* **236**, 515 (1956).
6. J. S. WAUGH and R.W. FESSENDEN, *J. Am. Chem. Soc.* **79**, 846 (1957).
7. R. McWEENY, *Molecular Phys.* **1**, 311 (1958).
8. C. E. JOHNSON and F. A. BOVEY, *J. Chem. Phys.* **29**, 1012 (1958).
9. A. A. BOTHNER-BY and C. NAAR-COLIN, *Ann. New York Acad. Sci.* **70**, 833 (1958).
10. R. U. LEMIEUX, R. K. KULLNIG, H. J. BERNSTEIN, and W. G. SCHNEIDER, *J. Am. Chem. Soc.* **80**, 6098 (1958).
11. J. N. SHOOLERY and M. T. ROGERS, *ibid.*, 5121.
12. G. V. D. TIERS, *Table of Characteristic N.M.R. Shielding Values.*
13. S. ALEXANDER, *J. Chem. Phys.* **28**, 358 (1958).
14. R. MORRIS, C. A. VERNON, and R. F. M. WHITE, *Proc. Chem. Soc.* 303 (1958).
15. J. A. POPLE, *Proc. Roy. Soc. A.* **239**, 541, 550 (1957).
16. P. C. LAUTERBUR.
17. L. M. JACKMAN and R. H. WILEY, *Proc. Chem. Soc.* 196 (1958).
18. J. A. ELVIDGE and L. M. JACKMAN, *ibid.* 89 (1959).
19. J. A. ELVIDGE, *J. Chem. Soc.* 474 (1959); and private communication.
19a. J. W. K. BURRELL, L. M. JACKMAN, and B. C. L. WEEDON, *Proc. Chem. Soc.* 263 (1959).
20. D. Y. CURTIN, H. GRUEN, and B. A. SHOULDERS, *Chem. and Ind.* 1205 (1958).
21. O. BASTIANSEN, *Acta Chem. Scand.* **3**, 408 (1949).
22. O. BASTIANSEN, *ibid.* **4**, 926 (1950).
23. S. BROWNSTEIN, *J. Am. Chem. Soc.* **80**, 2300 (1958).
24. S. GOODWIN, J. N. SHOOLERY, and L. F. JOHNSON, *Proc. Chem. Soc.* 306 (1958).
25. C. REID, *J. Am. Chem. Soc.* **78**, 3225 (1956).
26. C. RFID, *J. Molecular Spectroscopy* **1**, 18 (1957).

INDEX

Absorption of radio frequency power, 8
Absorption signal, 33
  detection of, 33, 34
Acetone dimethyl ketal, 54
Acetophenone, 123
Acetylacetone, 70
11-α-Acetoxyprogesterone, 104
Acetylenes, 60
  diamagnetic anisotropy of, 17, 112
  shielding by, 112
N-Acylamino acids, 72
Alcohols, 55
Aldehydes, 57, 62
Allenes, 60
Amides, 56, 72
  hindered rotation in, 103
Amines, 56, 72
  effect of pH on proton exchange rate, 72
Angular momentum of nucleus, 1
Azulene, 62

Benzaldehyde, 123
Benzene, 63
  diamagnetic anisotropy of, 18, 115, 125
  mono-substituted, 63
Bulbocapnine, 127
n-Butyraldehyde, spectrum, 98

Calibration of spectra, 41
  against external reference, 44
  against internal reference, 45
  by audiofrequency modulation, 43
  by the "wiggle beat" method, 43
  factors influencing the accuracy of, 43
Carbon (^{13}C), 77
  chemical shifts, 78
  natural abundance, 77
Carboxylic acids, 58
β-Carotene, 58
Carotenoids, 109
Chemical exchange, 26
  between water and ethanol, 28
  effect on spin-spin multiplicity, 26
  in amines, 72
  in ethanol, 26
  in pyrrole, 72
Chemical shift, 15, 50
  parameters,
    for fluorine, 48
    for protons, 46
p-Chloroiodobenzene, spectrum of, 95
Citral a and b, 125

Conformational analysis by n.m.r., 99
  of 1-cyano-2:2-difluoro-1:1:2-tribromo-
    ethane, 101
  of cyclohexane derivatives, 115
  of isobutyl bromide, 101
  of methyl methacrylate dibromide, 101
  of sugars, 116, 118
  use of spin-spin coupling constants for, 84,
    118
Conformation of α:β-unsaturated carbonyl
  compounds, 122
Conjugation, effect of,
  on allylic protons, 61
  on olefinic protons, 58
  on spin-spin coupling constants, 24
Cyclic compounds, 51
Cycling, 36
Cycloheptanone, 57
Cyclohexanone, 57
Cycloparaffins, 52
Cyclopentanone, 57

Deuterium exchange, 71, 80
  resonance, 80
Diamagnetic anisotropy, 19, 108
  of acetylene, 17, 112
  of benzene, 18, 115, 125
  of carbon—carbon double bonds, 129
  of carbon—carbon single bonds, 117
  of carbon—halogen bonds, 54
  of carbonyl groups, 122
Diamagnetic shift, 51
cis- and trans-dibromoethylenes, 119
trans-1:2-Dibromocyclopropane, 84
Dicentrine, 127
2:5-Dichloronitrobenzene, spectrum, 93
Diethyl ether, 54
  spectrum, 98
Diethyl ketone, spectrum, 98
1:1-Difluoroethylene, proton spectrum, 24
  spin-spin coupling in, 24
2:3-Dihydrofuran, 62
  coupling constants in, 87
  spectrum of, 88
Dihydropyran, 62
Di-isopropyl ketone, spectrum, 97
Dimethyl acetylene-dicarboxylate,^{13}C spectrum
  79
cis-cis-Dimethyl muconate, spectrum, 95
trans-trans-Dimethyl muconate, spectrum, 95
2:4, Dinitrochlorobenzene, spectrum, 93
2:4-Dinitrophenylhydrazones, 62
Dioxan, 55
Diphenylcyclopentanes, 126

Diphenyls, 126
Dispersion signal, 33
  supression of, 33
Double resonance, *see* spin de-coupling

Electron couples spin-spin interactions, *see*
  spin-spin coupling
Electron spin, 2
Enol ethers, 62
Epoxides, 55
Equivalent nuclei, 19
Esters, 55, 58
Ethanol, chemical exchange in, 26
  proton spectra, 20, 25, 26, 27
  spin-spin coupling in, 20, 26
Ethers, 55
Ethylbenzene, 58

Feist's acid, 105
Field contours, 37
  alteration by cycling, 36
Fluorine chemical shifts, 76
  theory of, 75
  resonance, 75
  dependence of frequency on solvent, 76
Furan, 64
  substituted, 64

Geometric isomerism, 120
Geranic acids, 125
Glyoxaline, 65
Gyromagnetic ratio, 6

Helmholtz coils, 32
Heterocycles (aromatic), 64
Hindered rotation, *see* conformational analysis
Homogeneity, 35
  dependence, on field contours, 36, 37
    on sample spinning, 36
Hydrocarbons, saturated, 52
Hydrogen bonding, 66
  concentration dependence of, 66
  in alcohols, 69
  in carboxylic acids, 71
  in enols, 71
  in methanol, 67
  in phenols, 69
  intramolecular, 68
  solvent dependence of, 68
  temperature dependence of, 67
11α-, and 11β-Hydroxypregnene-3:10-dione, 53
Hydroxylic protons, 66

Integration of signals, 49
Intensities of absorption bands, 20, 105
  measurement of, 48, 105
Internal reference, 45
  cyclohexane as, 46
  equivalence with external reference at infinite
    dilution, 47
  necessary properties, 46
  tetramethyl silane as, 46
  validity of use of, 50

Internal rotation, 28
  in substituted ethanes, 99
Isopropenyl bromide, 119
Isopropylbenzene, 58

Ketones, 57
  $\alpha:\beta$-unsaturated, 123

Lattice, definition of, 9
Leakage (r.f.), 33
Limonin, 64
Line positions, dependence on volume suscepti-
  bility, 44
  dependence on concentration, 46
Line shapes, relation to field contour, 37
Line width, 9
  at half-height, 36
Local diamagnetic currents, 16
Local paramagnetic currents, 75
Longitudinal relaxation, *see* spin-lattice relax-
  ation

McConnell's equation, 113
Magnet, 30
  electro-, 31
  permanent, 31
Magnetic, field sweep, 32
  moment, *see* nuclear magnetic moment,
  shielding, 14
    by interatomic diamagnetic currents, 16, 19
    by local diamagnetic currents, 16
    by paramagnetic currents, 16, 17
    effect of electronegativity on, 16, 75, 76, 78
    field strength dependence of, 19
    in acetylene, 17
    in aldehydes, 17
    in benzene, 18
    of atoms, 15
    of nuclei other than protons, 20, 74
    of protons, 14
    theories of, 15–20, 112
Mesityl oxide,
  spectrum, 84
Metal hydrides, 74
Methylamine, 73
  effect of pH on spectrum of aqueous, 73
Methyl benzoate, 123
3-Methylbutan-1-ol, spectrum, 97
Methyl *trans*-crotonate, 108
  spectrum of, 95
Methylcyclohexane, spectrum, 97
Methyl ethyl ketone diethylene ketal, 54
Methyl groups, determination of C-Me, 105
  in aldehydes, 57
  in alkyl halides, 54
  in amides, 57
  in amines, 57
  in aromatic compounds, 58
  in carotenoids, 109
  in cyclic compounds, 51
  in esters, 55, 57
  in ethers, 55

Methyl groups—*contd.*
in ketones, 57
in olefins, 58
in saturated hydrocarbons, 52
in steroids, 104, 129
N-Methylmorpholine, 55
Molecular beam techniques, 3
Muconic acids, 124

Naphthalene, spectrum, 95
Nitrites, hindered rotation in, 103
Nitrogen (^{14}N) resonance, 79
3-Nitrosalicyclic acid, spectrum, 93
Nitrosamines, hindered rotation in, 103
3-Nitro-*o*-xylene, spectrum, 93
Norpinane, 129
Nuclear, electric quadrupole moment, 1, 2
table of, 75
induction method, 34
magnetic resonance spectroscopy, theory, 6
magneton, 6
Nuclear spin, 1, 3
number, 1
table of, 75
states, 1, 6
distribution of, 8
probability of transitions between, 8
systems, 89
symbolism of, 89
AB, 89
ABX, 90
ABX$_3$, 91
ABC, 91
AB$_2$, 92
A$_2$X$_2$, 92
A$_2$B$_2$, 94
AB$_3$, 95
A$_2$B$_3$, 96
AB$_2$X$_2$, 96
A$_2$B$_2$X, 96

Olefins, 58, 60
Oxygen, effect on resolution, 35
resonance (^{17}O); 79

Paramagnetic, broadening, 12
shift, 51
Phenanthrene, 128
Phenols, 61
2-Phenylbutane, 51
Phosphorus (^{31}P)
determination of chemical shifts, 77
empirical shielding theories, 77
Phytol, 124
α- and β-Pinenes, 129
Polycyclic aromatic hydrocarbons, 62, 128
Polymethylenebenzenes, 18, 52
Precessional motion, 2
of nuclei, 2, 7
Propylene oxide, 55
Propylenes, 2-substituted, 120

Pyranosides, pentacetyl, 86
Pyrazole, 65
Pyridine, 64
Pyrrole, 64, 72
Pyrrolidine, 56
Pyrrolidone, 56

Quadrupole, broadening, 13
moment, *see* Nuclear electric quadrupole
moment
relaxation, 13, 73
effect on spin-spin multiplets, 26
Quantisation of angular momentum, 1
Quaternary ammonium salts, 56

Radiofrequency,
field, 31
resolution into components, 32
oscillator, 31
Reference, *see* external and internal reference
Relaxation processes, 8
influence on line width, 9
spin lattice, *see* spin-lattice relaxation
spin-spin, *see* spin-spin relaxation
Resolution, index of, 35, 40
Ringing, 38

Sample spinning, 38
Saturation, 13
broadening of resonance lines by, 14
dependence, on r.f. power, 41
on sweep rate, 40
factor, Z$_0$, 14
Second order splitting, 24
Semicarbazones, 62
Shielding constants, 59
Shielding, long range, 112
by aromatic rings, 115, 125
by carbon-carbon double bonds, 129
by carbon-carbon single bonds, 117
by carbon-carbon triple bonds, 114
by carbonyl double bonds, 122
in cyclohexane derivatives, 117
Shoolery's rules, 59, 110
Signal-to-noise ratio,
dependence on sweep-rate, 40
factors influencing, 40
Solvents, suitable, 48
Spectrometer (n.m.r.), 30, 34, 35
Spin decoupling, 4, 25
associated with efficient spin-lattice relaxation, 26
of interacting protons, 26
of ^{14}N in amides and pyrrole, 73
Spin number, *see* nuclear spin number
Spinning side bands, 38
Spin-lattice relaxation, 9
dependence on viscosity, 12
effect, on band shapes of spin-spin multiplets,
26
of paramagnetic substances on, 12
in liquids, 10
in solids, 10

Spin-lattice relaxation—*contd.*
    mechanism of, 10
    of nuclei possessing a quadrupole moment, 13
    time, T_1, 10
Spin-spin, multiplets (*see also* spin-spin coup-
        ling), rules for, 23
    in complex systems, 24
        coupling, 20, 83
        in ethanol, 20
        influence of quadrupole relaxation on, 72
        mechanisms of, 21, 22
        relation to field strength, 23
        rules for, 23
        theory of, 21
    coupling constant, J, 23
        dependence on conformation, 103
        dependence on stereochemistry, 84, 87
        in *trans*-1:2-dibromocyclopropane, 84
        in 2:3-dihydrofuran, 87
        in dimethyl β-methylmuconates, 87
        in ethyl groups, 87
        in isopropyl groups, 87
        in *cis*- and *trans*-olefins, 87
        in penta-acetylpyranosides, 86
        in propiolactone, 86
        table of, for H,H, 85
        table of, for H,F, 86
        values for ^{13}C,H, 79
        values for ^{14}N,H, 56, 72
        values for ^{31}P,H, 77
    relaxation,
        local field interactions and, 10
        mechanism of, 10
        spin exchange and, 10
        time, T_2, 11
    splitting, *see* spin-spin multiplets
Spin states *see* nuclear spin states

Spirilloxanthin, 108
Standardisation of spectra,
    against an external reference, 44
    against an internal reference, 45
    influence of solvent on, 45, 48
    influence of volume susceptibility on, 44
Stereochemistry,
    of cyclohexane derivatives, 115
    of sugars, 116
Steroids, 104
    Δ^7-dehydro, 129
cis and *trans*-Stilbenes, 126
Sulphonamides, 56
Sweep rate
    dependence of ringing on, 38
    dependence of saturation on, 38
    constancy of, 40

Tau (τ)-value, definition of, 47
Tetrahydrofuran, 55
Tetrahydropyran, 55
Thiols, 74
Thiophene, 64
    monosubstituted, 65
Toluene, and substituted toluenes, 58
Transverse relaxation, *see* spin-spin relaxation

α:β-Unsaturated esters, 121

n-Valeric acid, spectrum, 98
Volume magnetic susceptibility, 44

Wiggles, 38
    use as index of resolution, 40
Wiggle beats, 43
    use in measuring line separations, 43